Wilson Armis

Tales and Legends of the English Lakes

Wilson Armistead

Tales and Legends of the English Lakes

1st Edition | ISBN: 978-3-73407-848-4

Place of Publication: Frankfurt am Main, Germany

Year of Publication: 2019

Outlook Verlag GmbH, Germany.

TALES AND LEGENDS

OF THE

ENGLISH LAKES

BY THE LATE
WILSON ARMISTEAD
Author of "The Flora of Liverpool," etc.

LONDON: SIMPKIN, MARSHALL & CO
GLASGOW: THOMAS D. MORISON

1891

PREFACE.

No part of the world possesses so many charms for the contemplative mind as the admirable scenery of our English Lake District. None can furnish so wide a field for the excursions of a playful imagination, as those peaceful glens which are formed by the fantastic sweeps of our northern mountains.

The lover of nature, whose delight it is to traverse this romantic region, beholds here scenes the most lovely opening out on every hand. Mountains and dales wild enough, in all conscience, amidst which are hidden placid, silver lakes, embosomed in the most delicious, fairyland valleys, diversified with beautiful mansions, and snow-white cottages, nestling in all the luxuriance of their native woods and coppices.

It has been justly said that the district from Lancaster, and the Bay of Morecambe, to the borders of Scotland, includes in its territory the richest valleys, the wildest mountains, the dreariest moorlands, the greenest meadows, the most barren rocks, the thickest and most verdant woods, the sweetest towns and villages, the smoothest rivers, which the salmon loves to haunt; the most turbulent mountain streams, in whose dark pools, here and there, the speckled trout finds a dwelling-place; the gayest garden flowers, the loveliest heaths that ever grew wild, high hills, deep mines, noble families, and the loveliest maidens of the land.

Whether we contemplate the sublime grandeur of its mountains, or listen to the melodious murmurs of the distant waterfalls, or meditate along the margins of its woodland streams in the evening's calm, we must be enchanted with the scene, and feel fully prepared to exclaim with the poet:—

> "Lives there a man with soul so dead,
> As never to himself hath said,
> This is my own, my native land!"

The Lake District has long been regarded as the romantic "classic ground" of England. The Tour of Gray and others formerly, and the works and residence of some of the most celebrated poets of our day, have thrown a "sacred halo" around it in the eye of the stranger, endeared as it is by living and departed genius; and have exalted the enthusiasm with which the visitor surveys a region that embodies more variety of charming scenery, and of picturesque magnificence, than an equal space of our own or of any other country. In extent, indeed, the sister kingdoms may surpass it, but not in beauty; and, save in their "diadem of snow," its mountains may be said to rival the sublimity of the Alps, without their vastness. Where, in all Europe, in all the wide world, can more lovely and enchanting spots be found than are embosomed amongst the lakes and mountains of Cumberland and Westmorland?

The increased and increasing facilities afforded for visiting the unrivalled scenery of the Lake district, naturally excite a corresponding desire to supply the tourist with every incident connected with this interesting locality.

The great number of popular publications as Guides and Tours to the Lakes, which, at different intervals, have been eagerly received, is a striking proof of the patriotic interest that attaches to the district. These, though they are, many of them, replete with valuable information, and render the traveller much necessary aid, are most of them deficient in their allusion to the history and traditions of some of the more remarkable sites of this romantic region.

To supply this deficiency, in part, is the object of the present Work. The interest of a country abounding in spots the most attractive in themselves, is greatly enhanced by the local associations attaching to it, its connection with bygone days, be they of the historical or legendary kind; for,

> "Holier seems the ground
> To him who catches on the gale
> The spirit of a mournful tale,
> Embodied in the sound."

In the following pages are narrated a few of the romantic stories the country affords. The district, it is true, is not particularly rich in historical incidents; nor has it been the scene of many great events; yet, it has been justly said by a popular writer, what it wants in history it more than makes up in poetry.

True, it may appear to be richer in scenery than in legend, and in poetry than romance; but, the fact is, its legends and romance have been neglected. The district is highly suggestive of both, but it has had no Sir Walter Scott to make the most of them. A part of the land so famous for beauty and for song, independent of its Border proximity, is one peculiarly favourable to the lovers of old legends; its atmosphere is one in which fancy most delights to soar and to hover, and it contains a mine of materials for romance yet almost untouched.

The fierce feuds and stormful outgoings of the adjoining Borders, are full of interest and of romance peculiar to themselves. "Battles have assailed the banks" of nearly every stream—some of the strongholds yet remain, wherein the mosstroopers, clad in steel from head to foot, issued forth in the morning light—the hills are there, with the heath, across which they sped on gallant steeds, with lances outstretched, and gleaming helmets—the paths are yet green amid the dun moor along which they drove their spoil—and in solitary farm-houses, or lonely cottages, ancient dames may yet be met with, who can repeat, in song or story, the wild deeds which their mothers saw, and their sires performed.

Once there were more castles than churches in the country, to defend it from the Scot; and though these castles now, for the most part, stand solitary monuments of past ages and conditions of things, yet around them still linger the fame of heroic deeds, and the twilight melancholy of once absorbing woes. Besides its many other interesting monuments of antiquity, 'tis not without its aged monasteries and "ivy-mantled towers."

It has been truly said the spirit of romance is departing from the land in which we dwell. Our forests are felled where the freebooters of former days flourished—the fish are chased from our lakes by steamboats—the hills of heath, where the deer roved, are enclosed, and ploughed and harrowed over periodically—the green slopes and dusky dells, where nobles chased the roe, and the sunny glades of the forest into which they emerged, with gallant trains and bridles ringing, and their hunting gear glittering in the glorious sunlight of the olden time—all these are gone; and as we wander over the land, we find mostly drains and furrows, stone dykes, and straight fences, where the heather hung its blue bells unseen from year to year, save by the gorcock or the hare, or the myriads of wild bees that circled round the breathing flowers, and, humming within their tiny cells, sought out the sweet treasures which nature had hidden there. Our castles and abbeys are in ruins—our Border-keeps are mouldering to the ground—the battle grounds have been torn up by the plough—our briery glens and leafy shaws, consecrated by immortal song to past loves, have been ruthlessly desecrated—our ancient sports are at an end—we are a changed people—and the olden time is truly gone.

Let it never be thought that we rejoice not in the present because we regret the past. We feel, and are thankful for the blessings and comforts which the improved arts of the age impart to us; we exult in the progress of science throughout the land; we can even look with complacency upon a railroad, though it intersect, with its prosaic line, the woodlands where we first felt the poetry of life—though the very hawthorn, beneath which we breathed our vows of eternal fidelity to her who now lies nightly in our bosom, has been rooted up to prepare a path for it.

We see all this, and we think of it without regret. Our reason approving, consents to it; yet our imagination answers, "The spirit of romance is departing from us, and we sigh for the olden time."

Imagination is a faculty in which we delight, and phrenologists say that men are happy only in the active exercise of their faculties. Therefore it is, that, leaving the practical speculations of the arts and sciences, we have chosen to select a field wherein imagination may fly her boldest flight, and we have allowed our fancy to rove amid scenes of fictitious bliss or woe, or amidst the real sorrows and joys of many an "owre true tale."

I only add that, should the pleasure of the tourist be enhanced by a perusal of any of the following tales connected with the Lake district, it will confer a still greater pleasure on the writer, even than that of culling them, from time to time, during his visits to those nooks hallowed by poetry, or consecrated by history, which a frequent residence in this locality has afforded him the opportunity of exploring. They are offered to the lover of nature, and to the admirer of the picturesque, with the hope that, whilst delighting in nature's sublimities, which are self-evident, proclaiming, at every step, their Divine original, he may not pass by unheeded some of the remarkable spots of history or romance without feeling interested in their associations.

TALES AND LEGENDS

OF

ENGLISH LAKES.

HELWISE; OR, THE ILL-FATED LOVERS:

A TALE OF MUNCASTER HALL.

THOUGH ample testimony is borne to the simple and engaging manners of the Lake residents, I must confess there is a little Vandalism among them. They do not feel that generous love and veneration for the glorious remains of other years which ought to warm the breast of every Englishman. My uncle was indignant at the inattention paid to the scattered ruins of Penrith Castle.

"The Turks," he observed, "could only have turned the ruined habitations of the Christian nobles into cattle-sheds and pigstyes!"

We sat ourselves down at the edge of the moat, where the disgusting inroads of modern improvements would least obtrude themselves on our view, to contemplate the ruined strength and fallen grandeur of our ancestors. We were scarcely seated when an elderly gentleman, on whose countenance a cheerful good nature was visibly impressed, approached us. My uncle invited him to take a seat on our green sofa, with which invitation he smilingly complied.

My uncle, whose ideas were at least two centuries old, opened the conversation by an allusion to those times when our old northern castles shone in all their splendour; and their inhabitants possessed their original power.

"How much of their outward dignity have the higher classes lost," observed my uncle, "since literature and commerce have shed their genial influence on our favoured isle."

"Yes," replied the stranger; "and how much have the lower classes been elevated since that period. The ranks of society are less distinct; and the system of equality is perhaps as nearly realised as the well-being of society could admit."

"In some respects it may be so," said my father; "but I think that we might yet dispense with some of that pride which separates man from his brother man."

"If one may believe report," said my sister, "there was more love in former times than there is now. People were kinder then; men were more faithful; and unions in general more happy than they are at present."

"I can tell you a story on that subject," replied the stranger, "which will be interesting to the young people, and I hope no way disagreeable to old ones. For I count the person who cannot sympathise in a love story to be unfit for any social duty, and calculated for nothing but the cloister or the cell."

"By all means," exclaimed my sister, "let us hear it. If there be anything about the firm faith of a female heart, it will be pleasing."

"If there be anything," said my uncle, "about the manners of our ancestors, it will be instructive."

"If there be anything," said my father, "about the villany of man in it, it must be true."

"There will be something about all these," replied the stranger, and he now related the story.

It was customary in the times to which I allude, said our garrulous acquaintance, for the owners of these old halls and castles to retain each a jester in his mansion, called by the common people a fool. According to custom Sir Allan Pennington had a jester, whose name was Thomas Skelton, but whose common appellation was Tom Fool of Muncaster. But I shall have occasion to mention him in the course of my story; as he performed a tragical part in it—rather too much so, to be enumerated among the drolleries of a common jester. I will, however, give you the tale as I have often heard the parson repeat it to an old maiden aunt of mine, with whom I was brought up; and who never heard it without a copious flow of tears.

The morning was most delightful (this was the parson's uniform way of introducing the story), when the level beams of the sun first gleamed on the smooth surface of Devoke Water, and informed the joyous villagers that it was the First of May. The wooden clogs were stripped from the feet of the blooming damsels, and the leathern shoes, which had been carefully preserved from the preceding year, and many of which had adorned the feet of their mothers and grandmothers, were taken out of the paper which enveloped them. The oil with which they had been rubbed twelve months before was polished by the warm hand to a fine gloss. Every garden was robbed of its bloom to form garlands and chaplets in order to beautify what could not be beautified; for what—the parson would say, looking languishingly at my aunt

—could add beauty to a Cumberland maiden?

The Maypole was reared in a delightful meadow on the banks of Devoke Water; and the maidens blooming in beauty, and the youths bounding in health, repaired thither from the surrounding cottages. As the festive dance commenced, the soul of innocent gaiety began to expand. The festoons of flowers waving from the Maypole, and the garlands of the damsels, all gently agitated by a slight breeze, gave a gracefulness to the scene which no language can describe. It seemed as if the exhilarating breath of spring gave elasticity to the youthful limb, and a higher zest to the spirits, as the lively music gave emotion to the nimble feet of the light-footed dancers.

At the first pause in the dance every eye was attracted towards a most heavenly maiden, attired in the simple garb of a Cumberland shepherdess. She came tripping along the meadow in the full glow of her beauty, and, with a smile, joined the maiden circle. Every tongue was inquiring, "Wha is she?"—and every eye was eager to obtain a glance of her charms. Several of the most respectable shepherds offered to lead her to the dance, but she modestly refused. Among the rest Wild Will of Whitbeck, as he was generally called, urged her to favour him with her hand.

"I only came," said she, "to be a spectator of these innocent gaities; and, should I share in them, I should wish to procure a more modest partner."

"A modest partner!" exclaimed Will, "yan et darn't luik at ya: yan etle stand eating his thooms, and just whisperen la doon, 'will ya dance?' A poor feckless thing et darn't lait a sweetheart withoot its minny ga wi' it."

"You will please to leave me, shepherd," replied the maid, "and carry your raillery to other ears where it may be more agreeable."

"I'll hev a kiss furst," said Will, "for that canny feace and filed tongue hez quite laid ma ith brears."

"Forbear your rudeness, for God's sake," cried the damsel; "or you may repent it."

"By all the powers af love and beauty," exclaimed the carpenter's son, stepping up at that moment, "unless he stands off he shall repent it. Will you take a dance with me, fair maiden?"

She willingly complied. But the elder and more experienced part of the company said they observed a glance pass between them, which said they had met before. This renewed the inquiry who the damsel might be, but in vain. Will retired in a gloomy rage, swearing that he would discover who the girl was, and have revenge on the carpenter, if it cost him his life.

The lovers heard not his threats, but repaired to the Maypole; and, as they danced around it, sang the following roundelay:—

"What are monarchs' courts, my dear?
  Can their splendour yield them bliss?
Can the thrones and crowns of kings
  Yield a joy as sweet as this?
      Dancing round the Maypole!

Here no care or pain, my dear,
  Can into our bosom steal;
Heaven itself can scarce surpass
  Pleasures such as these we feel,
      Dancing round the Maypole!

Now, returning Spring, my dear,
  Wakes the birds on every spray—
We, whose hearts are formed for love,
  Sure may be as blithe as they.
      Dancing round the Maypole!

Hark the song of love, my dear,
  Every heart and tongue employ;
And shall we, less fond than they,
  Mix not in the general joy,
      Dancing round the Maypole!

Let our glowing hearts, my dear,
  Revel in the burning bliss;—
Speak our feelings through our eyes,
  And seal our union with a kiss,
      Dancing round the Maypole!"

Various were the conjectures respecting the unknown shepherdess; though all the country maids agreed that she was not what she seemed.

"Be wha she will," said Wild Will of Whitbeck, "I'll hunt it oot."

"She's niver worth it," observed a girl, who probably thought Will might employ his time better. But Will was not to be driven from his purpose. And some of those who had been refused by the fair unknown urged Will to make his promise good. Therefore, when the evening drew on, and the young people began to pair off towards home, Will, and two of his companions who were not more agreeably occupied, followed Richard, the carpenter's son, and his lovely partner, towards home. But little did they expect to see her sheltered in Muncaster Hall. As the lovers stood exchanging vows of eternal constancy at the garden gate, their pursuers heard enough to inform them that the maid was Helwise, daughter of Sir Allan Pennington; and to convince them that their faith was mutually plighted.

"Noo," said Will, "I hev him o' the hip. For Sir Ferdinand Hoddleston, of Millum Castle, wants et wed that leddy; an' if I yance let him kna et this silly carpenter follows her, he'll meak an example on him."

When Will informed the neighbours next Sunday of his discovery, they were struck with astonishment at the handsome young carpenter's audacity, as they termed it. The young women hoped and trusted that Sir Allan would never know; for it would be a pity that so nice a young man should be hanged—as he was sure to be, if Sir Allan knew that he courted his daughter. At the same time they thought he might have been content with one of the shepherd girls; yet it was hard he should be hanged for love. He deserved to be sent out of the country, the young men observed. The maidens thought it would be a pity to send him away; but they might put him in a nunnery, or something of that sort.

Wild Will of Whitbeck gave no opinion on the subject—his plans were deeper. He knew Sir Ferdinand and his temper well. He had often attended him in his sporting excursions; and, owing to his never-failing flow of rustic wit, could any time find admittance at Millum Castle, where his drolleries would beguile Sir Ferdinand of a melancholy hour. Will, therefore, adopted this plan to make Sir Ferdinand the avenger of the insult he had received from the carpenter, and the repulse he had met with from the lovely Helwise.

"We had fine spooart o'th first o' May," said Will; "but I got cruel ill vext."

"What happened to vex thee?" inquired Sir Ferdinand.

"Wya, ye see," said Will, "Sir Allan's daughter donned hersell like a country hoody, an thought et naebody could a kent her, but I kent her weel eneugh."

"And did that vex thee?" replied Sir Ferdinand.

"I sa her," replied Will, "an mear oor an' that, I followed em heam, an sa em give yan another a kiss. When she put her arms roond his neck, I war stark wood. What! war Dick better ner me?"

The train was now laid. Will had roused Sir Ferdinand's vengeance, without giving the least hint that he suspected such a thing.

"Shall I!" exclaimed Sir Ferdinand, as soon as Will had retired, "Shall I be made a fool of by a carpenter's son? Shall such a wretch as that presume to be my rival in the affections of the loveliest maid in Cumberland? Curse the idea! He shall be taught to know his duty better. No, I scorn to apply to Sir

Allan. I will be my own avenger. Were he removed I should be at peace. That will do. He dies!"

Once resolved, Sir Ferdinand felt no rest till his scheme was accomplished. The morning had scarcely dawned till he mounted and rode for Muncaster Hall. Few of the family were stirring when Sir Ferdinand arrived. Tom Fool, however, was up, and hastened to meet the knight, who had often expressed himself pleased with Tom's rustic wit.

"Good morning, Tom," said Sir Ferdinand, "what makes you laugh so this morning, Tom?"

"Lord Lucy's footman," replied Tom, "put a trick on me the last time he was here; and I have been paying him back what I owed him, for I would be in no man's debt."

"How hast thou managed thy revenge?" returned Sir Ferdinand.

"He asked me," said Tom, "if the river was passable; and I told him it was, for nine of our family had just gone over. ('They were nine geese,' whispered Tom, 'but I did not tell him that.') The fool set into the river, and would have been drowned, I believe, if I had not helped him out."

"If thou'lt revenge me of a scoundrel who lives here," said Sir Ferdinand, "I'll make a man of thee."

"You'll do what Sir Allan could never do, then," replied Tom, with a laugh. "But who is it, pray?"

"'Tis the carpenter," replied the knight.

"I owe him a grudge, too," said Tom; "for I put those three shillings which you gave me into a hole, and I found them weezend every time I went to look at them; and now they are only three silver pennies. I have just found out that Dick has weezend them."

"Then kill him, Tom, with his own axe, when he is asleep sometime; and I'll see that thou takes no harm for it," replied Sir Ferdinand.

"He deserves it, and I'll do it," said Tom.

"There's three crowns for thee," said Sir Ferdinand, "and he'll not weezen them, if thou follow my advice."

Tom wanted no further inducement. His own injuries, and the hopes of reward from Sir Ferdinand soon influenced him. And the next day, while the unsuspecting carpenter was taking his after-dinner nap, and dreaming probably of the incomparable beauties of his adorable Helwise, Tom entered the shed, and, with one blow of the axe, severed the carpenter's head fromhis body.

"There," said Tom to the servants, "I have hid Dick's head under a heap of shavings; and he will not find that so easily, when he awakes, as he did my shillings."

Sir Ferdinand was grievously disappointed in his scheme; for the lovely Helwise had buried her heart in the same grave that held the remains of her sleeping lover. It was in vain that Sir Ferdinand urged the tenderness and sincerity of his passion. She was deaf to his entreaties. Her heart was cold, and no human power could warm it. The noisy mirth of the hall she could hear unmoved; the mazy intricacies of the festive dance could not reanimate her; the glowing beauties of the summer landscape were gloomy and dull as December. She resolved to seclude herself from the giddy world, and brood over her own sorrows in a nunnery. She therefore retired to the Benedictine Convent of Maiden Castle—the ruins of which are still visible behind higher end of Soulby Fell; where she passed her few remaining days in piety and silent solitude.

The conscience of Sir Ferdinand left him no repose; and, to stifle recollections which became continually more insupportable, he joined the army, and soon after fell in the battle of Bosworth Field, fighting against the Earl of Richmond. He left a very handsome estate in the neighbourhood of Kirksancton to St. Mary's Abbey of Furness, to purchase masses for the repose of his own soul, and the soul of the young carpenter.

ST. HERBERT,

THE HERMIT OF DERWENTWATER.

AMONGST the beautiful isles of Derwentwater, that named St. Herbert's Island deserves a more than ordinary notice, as well for its beauty as its historical associations. This insulated paradise includes an extent of four or five acres, well covered with wood, and is situated near the centre of the lake. It obtained its name from St. Herbert, a priest and confessor, who, "to avoid the intercourse of man, and that nothing might withdraw his attention from unceasing mortification and prayer," about the middle of the 7th century, chose this island for his lonely abode.

"St. Herbert hither came,
And here for many seasons, from the world
Removed, and the affections of the world,
He dwelt in solitude."

The locality was well adapted to the severity of his religious life; he was surrounded by the lake, from whence he received his simple diet. On every hand the voice of waterfalls excited the most solemn strains of meditation—rocks and mountains were his daily prospect, inspiring his mind with ideas of the might and majesty of the Creator.

That St. Herbert had his hermitage on this island is certain from the authority of the venerable Bede, as well as from tradition, and nowhere could ancient eremite find more profound peace, or a place of so great beauty, whence to bear on the wings of imagination his orisons to heaven.

St. Herbert was particularly distinguished for his friendship to St. Cuthbert, bishop of Lindisfarne, with whom he was contemporary; and, according to a legendary tale, at the intercession of St. Herbert both these holy men expired on the same day, and in the same hour and minute, which, according to Bede, was in 678 or 687.

At Lindisfarne, expecting death,
The good St. Cuthbert lay,
With wasted frame and feeble breath;
And monks were there to pray.

The brotherhood had gathered round,
His parting words to hear,
To see his saintly labours crown'd,

And stretch him on the bier.

His eyes grew dim; his voice sunk low;
The choral song arose;
And ere its sounds had ceas'd to flow,
His spirit found repose.

At that same hour, a holy man,
St. Herbert, well renown'd,
Gave token that his earthly span
Had reach'd its utmost bound.

St. Cuthbert, in his early years,
Had led him on his way;
When the tree falls, the fruit itbears
Will surely, too, decay.

The monks of Lindisfarne meanwhile,
Were gazing on their dead;
At that same hour, in Derwent isle,
A kindred soul had fled.

There is but little information on record respecting St. Herbert, and had it not been for his intimacy with St. Cuthbert, his name probably would not have been handed down to posterity at all. In truth, he did little more than pray and meditate on this spot. It was his wish to live and die unknown. Though one in spirit, St. Cuthbert and the Hermit of Derwentwater were entirely dissimilar in character. St. Cuthbert was bishop of Lindisfarne, an eminent preacher in his day, whose eloquence influenced the will of many, and whose active zeal contributed to the advancement of the then dominant church, of which he was one of the main pillars and rulers. St. Herbert was altogether a man of prayer. He retired from the world to this solitude, and passed his days in devotion. The two saints used to meet once a year for spiritual communion. Which had most influence with the Ruler of heaven we cannot say.

The venerable Bede writes thus of the Hermit of Derwentwater:—"There was a certain priest, revered for his uprightness and perfect life and manners, named Herberte, who had a long time been in union with the man of God (St. Cuthbert of Farn Isle), in the bond of spiritual love and friendship. For living a solitary life in the isle of that great and extended lake, from whence proceeds the river of Derwent, he used to visit St. Cuthbert every year, to receive from his lips the doctrine of eternal life. When this holy priest heard of St. Cuthbert's coming to Lugubalia, he came after his usual manner, desiring to be comforted more and more, with the hope of everlasting blisse, by his divine exhortations. As they sate together, and enjoyed the hopes of heaven, among other things the bishop said:

"'Remember, brother, Herberte, that whatsoever ye have to say and ask of me, you do it now, for after we depart hence, we shall not meet again, and see one another corporally in this world; for I know well the time of my dissolution is at hand, and the laying aside of this earthly tabernacle draweth on apace.'

"When Herberte heard this, he fell down at his feet, and with many sighs and tears beseeched him, for the love of the Lord, that he would not forsake him, but to remember his faithful brother and associate, and make intercession with the gracious God, that they might depart hence into heaven together, to behold His grace and glory whom they had in unity of spirit served on earth; for you know I have ever studied and laboured to live according to your pious and virtuous instructions; and in whatsoever I offended or omitted, through ignorance and frailty, I straight-way used my earnest efforts to amend after your ghostly counsel, will, and judgment. At this earnest and affectionate request of Herbertes, the bishop went to prayer, and presently being certified in spirit that his petition to heaven would be granted,—

"'Arise,' said he, 'my dear brother, weep not, but let your rejoicing be with exceeding gladness, for the great mercy of God hath granted unto us our prayer.'

"The truth of which promise and prophecy was well proved in that which ensued; for their separation was the last that befel them on earth; on the same day, which was the 19th day of March, their souls departed from their bodies, and were straight in union in the beatific sight and vision; and were transported hence to the kingdom of heaven, by the service and hands of angels."

It is probable the hermit's little oratory or chapel might be kept in repair after his death, as a particular veneration appears to have been paid to this retreat, and the memory of the saint; for, at the distance of almost seven centuries, we find this place resorted to in holy services and processions, and the hermit's memory celebrated in religious offices.[1] The remains of the hermitage are still visible; and near to these hallowed ruins stands a small grotto of unhewn stone, called the New Hermitage, erected some years ago by Sir Wilfrid Lawson, to whose representative the island at present belongs. The dwelling of the anchorite consisted of two apartments, one of which, about twenty feet in length by sixteen in width, appears to have been his chapel; the other, whose dimensions are considerably less, was his cell.

The passion for solitude and a recluse life which reigned in the days of this saint, and was cherished by the monastic school, at first sight may appear to us uncouth and enthusiastic; yet when we examine into those times, our astonishment will cease, if we consider the estate of those men, who, under all the prejudices of education, were living in an age of ignorance, vassalage, and rapine; and we shall rather applaud than condemn a devotee, who, disgusted with the world and the sins of men, consigns his life to the service of the Deity in retirement. We may suppose we hear the saint exclaiming with the poet—

"Blest be that hand Divine, which gently laid
My heart at rest beneath this humble shade;
The world's a stately bark, on dangerous seas,
With pleasure seen, but boarded at our peril;
Here on a single plank, thrown safe on shore,
I hear the tumult of the distant throng,
As that of seas remote or dying storms;
And meditate on scenes more silent still,
Pursue my theme, and fight the fear of death.
Here, like a shepherd gazing from his hut,
Touching his reed or leaning on his staff,
Eager ambition's fiery chase I see;
I see the circling hunt of noisy men
Burst law's enclosures, leap the mounds of right,
Pursuing and pursued, each other's prey;
As wolves for rapine, as the fox for wiles,
Till Death, that mighty hunter, earths them all."

Young's *Excursion.*

Wordsworth has the following beautiful lines on the Hermit of Derwentwater:
—

"If thou, in the dear love of some one friend,
Hast been so happy that thou know'st what thoughts
Will sometimes, in the happiness of love,
Make the heart sink, then wilt thou reverence
This quiet spot; and, stranger, not unmoved
Wilt thou behold this shapeless heap of stones,
The desolate ruins of St. Herbert's cell.
There stood his threshold; there was spread the roof
That sheltered him, a self-secluded man,
After long exercise in social cares,
And offices humane, intent to adore
The Deity with undistracted mind,
And meditate on everlasting things
In utter solitude. But he had left
A fellow-labourer, whom the good man loved
As his own soul. And when, with eye upraised
To heaven, he knelt before the crucifix,
While o'er the lake the cataract of Ladore
Pealed to his orison, and when he paced
Along the beach of this small isle, and thought

Of his companion, he would pray that both
(Now that their earthly duties were fulfilled)
Might die in the same moment. Nor in vain
So prayed he! As our chroniclers report,
Though here the hermit numbered his last hours,
Far from St. Cuthbert, his beloved friend,
Those holy men died in the self-same day."

THE LOVERS' VOWS:

A TALE OF FURNESS ABBEY.

I CAN just remember the circumstance; it happened when I was a boy and went to Urswick school. Matilda—I will not mention her other name, because her friends are still living—Matilda was one of the loveliest females I ever knew. Her father had a small estate at ——, near Stainton; and she being his only child, he fondly imagined that her beauty and her fortune would procure her a respectable match. But alas! how often do your parents err in their calculations on the happiness which, they fondly imagine, will arise from the conduct of their children!

Matilda had accompanied James, a neighbouring farmer's son, to school, when infancy gave room to no other thoughts but those of play. James had ever distinguished the lovely Matilda for his playmate; for her he had collected the deepest tinged May gowlings that grew in the meadows below the village; he spared no pains to procure the finest specimens of hawthorn blossoms, to place in her bonnet; and would artlessly compliment her on her appearance under the flowery wreath. He was always ready to assist her in conning her lessons at school, and oftener wrought her questions than she did herself.

At an early age James was removed from school, and bound to an Ulverstone trader. Matilda and James met or heard of each other no more, till he had completed his eighteenth year, and the hard and active service in which he was employed had given his fine manly form an appearance at once imposing and captivating. Matilda, too, was improved in every eye, but particularly in James'. Never had James seen so lovely a maid as his former playmate. That friendship which had been so closely cemented in infancy, required very little assistance from the blind god to ripen it into love. Their youthful hearts were disengaged; they had neither of them ever felt an interest for any person, equal to what they had felt for each other; and they soon resolved to render their attachment as binding and as permanent, as it was pure and undivided.

The period had arrived when James must again trust himself to the faithless deep, when he must leave his Matilda to have her fidelity tried by other suitors; and she must trust her James to the temptation of foreign beauties. Both, therefore, were willing to bind themselves by some solemn pledge to live but for each other.

For this purpose, they repaired, on the evening before James' departure, to the ruins of Furness Abbey. It was a fine autumnal evening; the sun had set in the greatest beauty; and the moon was hastening up the eastern sky, through a track slightly interspersed with thin fleecy clouds, which added to its beauty, rather than impaired it. They knelt in the roofless quire, near where the altar formerly stood; and, fondly locked in each other's arms, they repeated, in the presence of heaven, their vows of deathless love. James was dressed in his best seaman's dress—a blue jacket, with a multitude of silver-plated buttons, and white trowsers; while Matilda leaned on his neck in a dress of the purest white muslin, carelessly wrapped in a shawl of light blue.

I have been thus particular, said the narrator in describing their dresses, because this is the picture I would paint:—I would sketch an east view of the abbey, looking in at the large east window, where two lovers were kneeling, folded in each other's arms—the moonbeams just striking upon the most prominent parts of their figures—the deep shadows occasioned by the broken columns and scattered fragments, should recede into the distance—the dark gray ruins, and the deep green and brown of the oaks, slightly but brilliantly gilded by the moon, should peep out of the lengthened gloom with sparkling effect. But on the figures I would bestow the greatest attention. What manly vigour I would give to his attitude! What sweetness, what loveliness to hers!

But what became of the betrothed lovers? Their fate was a melancholy one. James returned to his ship, and never returned from his voyage. He was killed by the first broadside of a French privateer, which the captain foolishly ventured to engage with. For Matilda, she regularly went to the Abbey to visit the spot where she last saw him; and there she would stand for hours, with her hands clasped on her breast, gazing on that heaven which alone had been witness to their mutual vows. Indeed, I think this would make a picture almost equal to the other. How fine a contrast would the light and fairy form of Matilda make with the broken fragments of the ruined Abbey; it would give a life and effect to the picture which you have no conception of. I am confident if you once drew a picture of this kind, you would never again sketch a scene without a story to it.

THE STONE OF WALLOW CRAG;

OR, THE POET OF KENTMERE.

CHARLES WILLIAMS was one of those individuals who are "born to blush unseen." It is probable, therefore, that his name is unknown, and that his merits might have slept in obscurity but for us. We suspect that he has never been heard of before, and it is very likely that he never will be again. Charles had no long line of ancestors whose merits he could impute to himself. His great-grandfather had, to be sure, been the most noted wrestler in his day; and had annually won the belt at Bowness and at Keswick, but his prowess was forgot by all but his immediate descendants; and even his hard-earned belts had long since been cut up for repairing cart gear. Though Charles was only the son of a small farmer, yet there was one thing on which the family prided itself—there was a W. W. over the kitchen door which

"Was a sartan sign," his mother argued, "et that hoos hed belengd to them sometime lang sen."

There was one circumstance which we ought not to omit; particularly as it excited no inconsiderable interest, at the time, through all the neighbourhood of Kentmere. On the very day, and as far as we can ascertain, at the very hour, when Charles was born, a huge stone, self-moved, rolled down Wallow Crag into Hawes Water! The old women could and would account for it no other way than that he was born to be droond. Mr. Gough, who was then beginning to exhibit the first dawning of that genius which has procured him the esteem and admiration of all true lovers of rational philosophy, would gladly have convinced them that it was nothing but the effects of a thaw which had taken place only a few days before. But they argued that

"Thear hed been many a tha afoar, but niver a stane rolled doon Wallow Crag afoar."

Charles however grew up to be a boy, just as if this ominous stone had continued to sit secure on the mountain's ridge. But it might be said of him that "a strange and wayward wight was he." While other boys were ranging through the woods in pursuit of bird-nests, Charles would stretch himself on a smooth-faced rock, and pore on the adjacent landscape like one half crazed. To retire into a lonely wood behind his father's house, and teach a little brook, which ran through it, to take a thousand fantastic forms, was to Charles the sweetest recreation he could enjoy. The perpetual wings of time had now spread fifteen or sixteen winters over the vale of Kentmere, since the stone rolled into Hawes Water, and Charles was grown a tall and graceful boy. The little time which his father had spared him to school, had not been misemployed by the active youth; and though he felt a diffidence about entering into conversation, it was generally allowed that, when he did unloosen his tongue, he could argue any man in the valley, except the parson, who never stopt to hear anybody speak but himself, and the schoolmaster, who never spoke at all.

One evening about this time, as Charles was returning from an accustomed ramble, where he had been enjoying a view of the mist slowly gathering among the mountain heads to the north, he was aroused from his reverie by a shrill scream; a young female had been pursuing a footpath over the adjoining field, and was at that instant closely followed by a neighbour's bull. Charles, with the speed of lightning, was at the girl's side; and, with a presence of mind oftener found in boys than men, he snatched the umbrella out of her hand, and unfurled it in the enraged animal's face. The astonished beast retreated a few paces, and, according to a standing rule among mad bulls, having been foiled in its first attempt, it did not make a second attack.

Charles, with that gallantry which is a concomitant of generous minds, proposed to see the affrighted maid to her father's dwelling. Maria was a girl whom Charles had known from her infancy; he had played with her at school, but he never before observed that she possessed anything superior to the other girls of the dale. But this evening, as she hung on his arm and thanked him with such a pair of soft blue eyes so kindly—as the colour varied so often on her cheek—and her bosom throbbed so agitatedly, he discovered that Maria possessed more charms than all the valley beside.

This evening's adventure formed an epoch in the life of Charles Williams. All his actions were now influenced by one all-powerful impulse. Ardent in his admiration of nature's charms, that ardour was now transferred from the general beauties of creation to the particular beauties of the lovely Maria. Indeed, Maria was peculiarly formed to please the fancy, and captivate the heart, of a youth like Charles. There was a symmetry in her limbs, an elegance in her person, and a simple gracefulness in her motions, which rendered her an agreeable object even to the most indifferent observer. But the charms of her mind were the gems on which be placed the highest value. There was a sombre shade of seriousness, perfectly distinct from melancholy, which none could behold without feeling interested. This seriousness, however, had nothing in it inimical to that lively joyance which gives so delicious a zest to our youthful days.

She even possessed a vivacity that accompanied all her actions, and threw her real character into the distance. Though endued with the keenest sensibility, she appeared all life and gaiety. Wherever she was, she was the soul of the little company—her lively wit and her smiling beauty procured her attention wherever she showed herself. This beautiful mixture of the gay and the grave assumed, on some occasions, such strange contrasts, that she seemed to be composed of inconsistencies. Often in her little evening rambles with her young companions, after having put them all in good humour with themselves and with one another, by her little flattering railleries and harmless frolics, she would in an instant bound away from the group with the elastic grace of a mountain nymph—abruptly enter the cottage of some sick or suffering neighbour, with a smile on her countenance, like the angel of comfort charged with blessings, kindly inquire after their various wants and distresses, soothe them with consolatory hopes of better days, offer all those little assistances which old and decaying age accepts so gratefully at the hands of youth, and after mingling a sigh or a tear with theirs, again join her gay companions as though nothing had occurred.

In the innocent society of this amiable maiden, Charles passed the sweetest hours of his existence. His former boyish pursuits were renounced. The windmill, on a rock at a little distance, though nearly matured, was never completed; the water-works in the wood were permitted to run to ruin, even the perpetual motion in the room over the old kitchen, which was in a state of great forwardness, was neglected for a time, and eventually relinquished.

It is supposed, our intelligent correspondent says, that if Charles had never been in love, it is probable that he had never been a poet. And in confirmation of this idea, we observe that his first productions are of the amatory kind —"odes to beauty," "lines to Maria," "acrostics," &c. Among these fragments, we found a little airy piece without a head but we suppose intended for Maria:

"If all the world was made of kisses,
And all those kisses were made forme,
And I was made for you, my love,
How happy we should be!

If all the graces were join'd in one,
And all the wit and beauty too,
They'd make a maid like you, my love,
They'd make a maid like you!"

Some of his lyric pieces exhibit a strange mixture of philosophy and passion, learning and love. In the eleventh page of the manuscript before us, we find as curious a specimen of this kind as we ever recollect. It is much interlined and seems never to have been finished.

ON LOVE.

"Newton's keen observant eye,
Found a power pervade creation;
Ignorant of when or why,
He fondly called it gravitation.

But 'tis love that binds the spheres—
Love's the real central-forces—
Wheels them round their varying years,
Impels them on, and shapes their courses.

Nature all abounds in love,
What is there but feels its power?
Hear it warbling in the grove!
See it blooming in a flower!

What's attraction, pray, but love?
And affinity's the same."

But the tender passion does not seem to have engrossed all his poetical powers, as we find several pieces both grave and gay on different subjects. One of these we shall select as it seems to possess some originality, and has been occasioned apparently by that influx of strangers which generally enlivens the lake district during the summer months; some of whom have probably noticed our mountain bard, if we may judge from one of the stanzas.

THE STRANGER AT THE LAKES.

"When summer suns lick up the dew,
And all the heavens are painted blue,
'Tis then with smiling cheeks we view,
    The stranger at the Lakes.

When morning tips with gold the boughs,
And tinges Skiddaw's cloud-kiss'd brows,
Then round the lake the boatman rows,
    The stranger at the Lakes.

When gray-rob'd evening steps serene,
Across the sweetly-varied green,
Beside some cascade may be seen
    The stranger at the Lakes.

Embosomed here the rustic bard,
Who oft has thought his fortune hard,
Is pleas'd to share the kind regard
Of strangers at the Lakes.

He whose ideas never stray
Beyond the parson's gig and gray,
Stares at the carriage and relay
Of strangers at the Lakes.

As by his cot the phæton flies,
The peasant gapes with mouth and eyes,
And to his wond'ring family cries,
'A stranger at the Lakes!'

Sometimes when brewers' clerks appear,
And Boniface is short of gear,
He says, 'Kind Sirs, we've had, this year,
Few strangers at the Lakes.'

At Christmas, Poll, the barmaid, shows
Her lustre gown and new kid shoes,
And says, 'I tipp'd the cash for those
From strangers at the Lakes.'

But could the post-horse neighing say
What he has suffer'd night and day,
'Tis much, I think, if he would pray
For strangers at the Lakes."

Time, it is said, has wings; but Charles never observed that it even moved, till he found himself in his twentieth year. That love which at first sought only to relieve itself in the society of its object, now began to assume a determined character. But to any but lovers, the description of love scenes would be irksome. It will be quite sufficient if we hint at the affair, and leave our readers to fill up the outline. We will only therefore assure them on the best authority, that Charles set out no less than three several times with a resolute determination to declare the full extent of his passion, and solicit the fair hand of Maria; and that as soon as he saw the maid, his purpose "dissolved like the baseless fabric of a vision;" that Charles at length conquered this timidity, and urged his suit with such ardour, that he was heard afterwards to say he believed love was like steam, the more it was compressed, the greater was its elasticity; that Maria received the declaration with all due bashfulness, and promised to be his bride as soon as she had completed her twenty-first year; that Charles, as is usual on such occasions, flew home on the wings of ecstasy, &c. It seems to have been about this time that the following birthday ode was written—perhaps while he was suffering under the effects of his own bashfulness:—

"Maria, this is just the day,
Some twenty years ago, they say,
You fill'd your mother's arms;
A little puling sprig of love,
So kindly dropp'd from heaven above,
To bless me with your charms.

Obeying custom, I intend
Some little birthday gift to send—
But stay, what must it be?
Of beauty you have quite a share,
Accomplish'd too, as well as fair,
And richer far than me.

I would not ever have it said,
I offer'd trinkets to the maid,
Which you might scorn to take;
I'll offer then no works of art;
I'll give you, love, an honest heart—
Pray, keep it for my sake."

Our correspondent says he would be happy if he could here conclude his narrative, as Sir Walter Scott does, with a happy marriage; for however delightful the transition from sorrow to joy may be, the reverse, even in description, has no charms. But poor Charles was doomed to be hurled from the height of his felicity to the lowest depths of despair. The joyful promise had scarcely escaped the lovely lips of Maria, and while her lover was yet giddy with his joy, when the amiable maid was attacked by a severe illness, which baffled all the doctor's skill. If entreaties for human or divine aid could have prolonged the existence of the ill-fated Maria, she had not died. Charles was ever at her pillow—his studies were relinquished—his poetry was neglected—and the dying Maria filled the whole extent of his capacious mind. But all was vain; the grisly monster Death had selected her as his victim, and he would not quit his hold; he was deaf alike to the lamentations of a parent, the regrets of friends, and the distractions of a betrothed lover.

Though every succeeding morning showed how great was the havoc that disease was making in her tender frame, and the period of her suffering was evidently approaching, Charles still hoped she would soon be well. If she was more than usually debilitated, he observed that the fever had left her, and she only wanted her strength recruiting, and they would then renew their walks. If the hectic flush overspread her cheeks, he hailed it as the sign of returning health. And thus he hoped even against hope. His reason would have convinced him she was dying, if reason had been allowed to speak; but he wished her to live, and he would not stoop to think that she would die. Thus he fulfilled the remarks of the poet—

> "We join in the fraud, and ourselves we deceive,
> What we wish to be true, love bids us believe."

When at last the pale hue of death overspread her once-blooming cheek, when she turned her languid eye towards her lover and faltered "farewell," when she closed her faded eyes and expired in prayer, Charles stood by the bedside like a being bereft of power and motion. The deepest despair overwhelmed him—his hopes were blasted—his fond creation of future bliss was in an instant destroyed, and his mind received a shock too powerful for nature to sustain.

From this moment a smile was never seen to illuminate his features, the most gloomy and secluded places were his favourite haunts. He avoided society as if the breath of man was pestilential; and occupied his time in brooding over his own melancholy. In his manuscript we find a number of melancholy effusions, which were evidently written about this time; and clearly bespeak a mind bordering on the gloomy verge of insanity. But as they are some of them by far the best pieces in the collection—a proof that poetry and madness are nearly allied—we will select two which tend to illustrate the awful state of the writer's mind.

THE EVENING WALK.

"How soothing to the soul the shade
  Which evening spreads around!
How bright the dewy gems that braid
  The foliage of the ground.

No sound is heard thro' ether wide,
  From hill or coppice green,
Save where the streamlet seems to chide
  The stillness of the scene.

Contagion catches on the soul,
  And lulls e'en grief to rest;
No more contending passions roll
  Along the troubled breast.

I seem a moment to have lost
The sense of former pain;
As if my peace had ne'er been crost,
Or joy could spring again.

But ah! 'tis there!—the pang is there;
Maria breathes no more!
So fond, so constant, kind, and fair,
Her reign of love is o'er.

No more through scenes like these shall we
Together fondly stray;
Till night itself would seem to me
More genial than the day.

I feel the cold night's gathering gloom
Infect my throbbing breast;
It tells me that the friendly tomb
Alone can give me rest.

I then shall sleep the sleep serene,
Where she so long has slept;
Nor be the wretch I long have been,
Nor weep as I have wept."

THE CHURCHYARD.

"Here, then, my weary head shall rest,
Here weep and sigh alone;
And press the marble to my breast,
And kiss the senseless stone.

I'm calmer now—a silv'ry sound
Is whisp'ring in my ear;
That tells me this is sacred ground,
And she is hov'ring near.

Celestial stillness reigns around,
Serenely beats my breast;
Maria's spirit treads this ground,
And hushes me to rest.

I see Maria hov'ring there—
She waves her wings of light;
Angelic music fills the air,

And charms the ear of night.

Stay, lovely maiden, longer stay,
And bless thy lover's eyes;
And do not soar so fast away
To seek thy native skies.

'Tis gone—the lovely vision's gone!
And night's dim shades prevail;
Again, I feel myself alone,
And pour my fruitless wail.

I seem like one who madly raves
Among the silent dead;
And start to hear the hollow graves
Re-echo to my tread.

But I shall soon forget my woes,
And dry my ev'ry tear,
And rest as unconcern'd as those
Who sleep serenely here."

So far from having a salutary effect upon the mind of Charles, time seems only to have increased the despondency that had enveloped and clouded the reasoning faculties of our poet. We find, in a subsequent part of the volume, the following lines, which show that his mind was giving way under the pressure of acute distress:—

"Ah! tell me not of busy life—
Its bustling folly—joyless strife—
Can these dispel my care?
No—let me seek some cavern drear,
Where not a sound can meet my ear,
But groans of death, and shrieks of fear,
The music of despair?

The black'ning storm, the driving rain,
Shall cool the fever in my brain,
And lull me to repose:
Then, when the thunders o'er me roll,
And spirits scream and goblins howl,
The tempest shall compose my soul,
And cheat me of my woes."

About six months did Charles continue in this deplorable condition, attracting the sympathy of all who beheld him. And often when he passed the cottage doors, where, in happier days, he had accompanied Maria on her errands of benevolence, the objects of his former bounty would look after him with a sigh, and say, "Poor Charles! Poor Charles!"

Though he generally spent the day in rambling about the woods and hills, the hour of his return seldom exceeded that of nightfall. One evening, however, he delayed his return; his parents made every enquiry, but in vain. He had been seen on Harter-fell in the afternoon, but no further tidings could be obtained. Early next morning the melancholy suspicion was confirmed—he was found drowned. It is rumoured in the vale, says our friend, but he will not vouch for its truth, that he was found in the very spot where the stone rolled down when he was born. It appears that he had meditated this act from the following lines, which shall conclude our extracts:—

> "And what is death, that I should dread
> To mingle with the silent dead?
> 'Tis but a pang—and pangs are o'er;
> A throb—and throbbing is no more;
> One struggle—and that one my last:
> A gasp—a groan—and all is past!"

THE SKULLS OF CALGARTH.

A LEGEND OF WINDERMERE LAKE.

THIS old mansion of Calgarth, on the banks of Lake Windermere, is built much in the style of Levens and Sizergh. Some of the rooms have been elegantly finished; but, having been a long time in the possession of farmers, who occupy but a part of it, it is much gone out of repair, and has, on the whole, a melancholy appearance. This circumstance, in concurrence with the superstitious notions which have ever been common in country places, and the particular mentioned hereafter, have probably given rise to a report, which has long prevailed, that the house is haunted. And many are the stories of frightful visions and mischievous deeds which the goblins of the place are said to have performed, to terrify and distress the harmless neighbourhood. These fables are not yet entirely disbelieved. Spectres still are seen, and there are two human skulls, which have lain in the window of a large room as long as can be remembered, whose history and reputed properties are too singular not to contribute something to this story of "the haunted house," and to let them be passed over in this route.

It has been a popular tale in these parts of immemorial standing, that these skulls formerly belonged to two poor old people, who were unjustly executed for a robbery; to perpetuate their innocence, some ghost brought them there; and that they are, for that end, indestructible, and in effect, "immoveable." For, it is said, to what place soever they were taken, or however used, they were still presently seen again in their old dormitory, the window. As the report goes, they have been buried, burned, powdered, and dispersed in the winds, and upon the lake, several times, to no purpose as to their removal and destruction: so far, says common fame. Certain it is these human remains still exist, and it would be thought an impeachment of the taste and curiosity of the nymphs and swains of the neighbouring villages, if they could not say they had once seen the skulls of Calgarth.

As a more rational account of the matter (though still lame and unsatisfactory), it is told by some, that there formerly lived in the house a famous doctress, who had two skeletons by her, for the usual purposes of her profession; and the skulls happening to meet with better preservation than the rest of the bones, they were accidentally honoured with this singular notice. But, be their origin what it may, their legend is too whimsical and improbable to deserve being recorded, otherwise than as an instance of the never-failing credulity of ignorance and superstition.

THE LUCK OF EDEN HALL.

A TALE OF THE MUSGRAVES.

EDEN HALL, the seat of the chief of the famous border clan of Musgrave, is a large and handsome edifice, on the west bank of the river Eden, built in the taste which prevailed about the time of the Charles's. Being bordered with trees, it forms an elegant feature in the pleasure grounds. There is here preserved, with scrupulous care, an old and anciently-painted glass goblet, called the "Luck of Edenhall," which would appear, from the following traditionary legend, to be wedded to the fortunes of its present possessors. The butler, in going to procure water at St. Cuthbert's well, in the neighbourhood (rather an unusual employment for a butler) came suddenly upon a company of fairies, who were feasting and making merry on the green sward. In their flight they left behind this glass, and one of them returning for it, found it in the hands of the butler. Seeing that its recovery was hopeless, she flew away, singing aloud—

"If that glass should break or fall,
Farewell the luck of Eden Hall."

The connection of the prosperity of the family with the integrity of an inanimate object, has frequently been one of the playthings of tradition, and traces of the superstition are found in ancient fable. There is a legend of this kind attached to a pear, preserved in a silver box at Coalstoun, the seat of the Earl of Dalhousie, near Haddington; and there is or was, a glass cap at Muncaster castle, given by Henry VI. to Sir John Pennington, which, from the general opinion of the King's sanctity, and that he entailed with the gift a blessing on the family, was called "the Luck of Muncaster."

The initials, I. H. S., are marked upon the case containing the goblet at Eden Hall, sufficiently showing the sacred uses to which it was originally appropriated. Philip, Duke of Wharton, alludes to it in his ballad, called—

THE DRINKING MATCH OF EDEN HALL.

"God prosper long, from being broke,
  The 'Luck of Eden Hall!'
A doleful drinking bout Ising,
  There lately did befal.

To chase the spleen with cup and cann,
Duke Philip took his way;
Babes yet unborn shall never see
The like of such a day.

The stout and ever-thirsty duke
A vow to God did make;
His pleasure within Cumberland
Those live-long nights to take.

Sir Musgrave, too, of Martindale,
A true and worthy knight;
Estoon with him a bargain made
In drinking to delight.

The bumpers swiftly pass about,
Six in an hand went round;
And, with their calling for more wine,
They made the hall resound.

Now, when these merry tidings reach'd
The Earl of Harold's ears,
And am I, quoth he, with an oath,
Thus slighted by my peers?

Saddle my steed, bring forth my boots,
I'll be with them right quick,
And, master sheriff, come you too,
We'll know this scurvy trick.

Lo, yonder doth Earl Harold come,
Did one at table say:
'Tis well, reply'd the mettl'd Duke,
How will he get away?

When thus the Earl began:—Great Duke,
I'll know how this did chance,
Without inviting me:—sure this
You did not learn in France.

One of us two, for this offence,
Under the board shall lie:
I know thee well; a Duke thou art,
So some years hence shall I.

But trust me, Wharton, pity 'twere
So much good wine to spill,

As those companions here may drink,
  Ere they have had their fill.

Let thou and I, in bumpers full,
  This grand affair decide,
Accurs'd be he, Duke Wharton said,
  By whom it is deny'd.

To Andrews, and to Hotham fair,
  Then many a pint went round:
And many a gallant gentleman
  Lay sick upon the ground.

When, at the last, the Duke found out
  He had the Earl secure,
He ply'd him with a full pint-glass,
  Which laid him on the floor.

Who never spake more words than these,
  After he downwards sunk;
My worthy friends, revenge my fall,
  Duke Wharton sees me drunk.

Then, with a groan, Duke Philip held
  The sick man by the joint;
And said, Earl Harold, stead of thee,
  Would I had drank this pint.

Alack, my very heart doth bleed,
  And doth within me sink!
For surely a more sober Earl
  Did never swallow drink.

With that the sheriff, in a rage,
  To see the Earl so smit,
Vow'd to revenge the dead-drunk peer
  Upon renowned St. Kitt.

Then stepp'd a gallant squire forth,
  Of visage thin and pale;
Lloyd was his name, and of Gany Hall,
  Fast by the river Swale;

Who said, he would not have it told
  Where Eden river ran,
That, unconcerned, he should sit by,
  So, sheriff, I'm your man.

Now, when these tidings reach'd the room,
  Where the Duke lay in bed,
How that the squire thus suddenly
  Upon the floor was laid:

O heavy tidings! quoth the Duke,
  Cumberland thou witness be,
I have not any captain, more
  Of such account as he.

Like tidings to Earl Thanet came,
  Within as short a space,
How that the under sheriff, too,
  Was fallen from his place.

Now God be with him, said the Earl,
  Sith 'twill no better be;
I trust I have within my town
  As drunken knights as he.

Of all the number that were there,
  Sir Rains he scorned to yield;
But, with a bumper in his hand,
  He stagger'd o'er the field.

Thus did this dare contention end,
  And each man of the slain
Were quickly carried off to sleep,
  Their senses to regain.

God bless the King, the Duchess fat,
  And keep the land in peace;
And grant that drunkenness henceforth
  'Mong noblemen may cease!" &c.

J. H. Wiffen wrote a short poem upon the "Luck of Eden Hall," and the German poet, Upland, has a ballad upon the same subject.

The Musgraves are a family of great antiquity and reputation. They came to England with the Conqueror, and settled first in Musgrave, in Westmoreland; then at Hartley Castle, in the same county; and, finally, at their present residence at Eden Hall. Sir Philip Musgrave, who was commander-in-chief of the king's troops for Cumberland and Westmoreland, in the Parliamentary war, just walks across the stage in Scott's legend of Montrose; but, by mistake the novelist calls him Sir Miles.

THE MAID OF HARDRA SCAR;

OR, THE MYSTERIOUS STRANGER.

IN the early part of the summer of 1807, a very handsome young lady, apparently about twenty-two, came to the village of Hawes, and took lodgings there. She positively refused to tell either her name or the place of her residence. Her manners were highly accomplished, though her behaviour sometimes assumed a degree of wildness and incoherence, which raised doubts as to the state of her mind. Her dress was rather rich than splendid; and white was her customary attire. A broad pink ribbon was always tied round her waist, with two ends behind, reaching to her feet. It was observed that she took particular pleasure in seeing these ribbons flutter in the wind, as she rambled over the adjoining fells. Curiosity, that busy personage in most places, and particularly so in the village of Hawes was eager to trace the history of the mysterious visitor, but in vain. The most distant allusion to the subject always produced silence.

Some supposed that she was a young lady who had been crossed in love, and had fled hither to brood over her disappointment in solitude; indeed her conduct rather sanctioned such an opinion, for she kept no company. When she saw any one, it was to administer relief or to enquire after their wants.

Others thought she might be some young widow, who had chosen to linger out her existence in obscurity in such a secluded spot as that. This opinion did not want support for she was constant in her visits to all the widows in the village, beside lodging with one.

Others again thought she was betrothed to some military officer, and chose to escape the importunities of other lovers, by hiding herself here till peace should restore her future husband to her arms.

Such were a few of the many surmises which at that time constituted the tea-table gossip at Hawes. Though each party felt confident that its own opinion was right, it remained only vague conjecture; for the young lady herself never dropped a single hint which could in the least turn the scale of imagination to the side of certainty.

One evening, having taken her accustomed ramble, she did not return; and the widow with whom she lodged became extremely impatient and uneasy. Inquiries were made in all directions, but no one had seen her. Several young men volunteered to search her usual haunts, but nothing could be found.

For several weeks, and even months, the sudden disappearance of the fair stranger continued to occupy the principal attention of the village. Nor will this appear surprising, when you recollect that only seldom anything occurs in a place like that of a romantic nature; yet the hearts of the inhabitants are as open to the sympathies of humanity in that place as in others.

At last it was remembered that a carriage, with the blinds up, had called to water the horses at Mr. Clark's on that evening; and had driven forward without any one alighting. At the time it was considered to be an empty carriage; but when the fair stranger was found to have disappeared so mysteriously the same evening, it was concluded that she had been carried off by her friends in this very carriage.

Without attempting to explain how this was, she was never heard of after that day.

The picture I would draw from this story is simply this:—One of her usual walks was up the glen to Hardra waterfall. Every day, when the weather would permit, did she traverse this glen. After viewing the immense column of water which there is precipitated over the projecting rock into the unfathomable cistern at its foot, she would ascend the steep acclivity which leads to the top of the rock. Upon a natural rude column of stone on the left hand side, which appears to have been torn from the parent rock during some convulsion of nature, would she stand for hours, her long pink ribbons fluttering in the mountain breeze. I know of no finer subject than this for a picture. The broken and overhanging rocks—the loose fragments at their feet —the cascade itself, the finest in the country—the brook fretting and foaming down the rugged glen—the stunted trees, and matted foliage, which protrude from the fissures of this natural wall—the huge erect pillar of stone, which rears its detached mass above the adjoining rock—and one of the loveliest females I ever saw, attired in flowing white drapery, which, with the ribbons, fluttered and played upon the wind—could you find a subject equal to this for interest, one equal to it for sublimity and beauty?

THE TWO BROTHERS.

A TALE OF ENNERDALE.

"THESE Tourists, heaven preserve us! needs must live
A profitable life: some glance along,
Rapid and gay, as if the earth were air,
And they were butterflies to wheel about
Long as the summer lasted: some, as wise,
Perch'd on the forehead of a jutting crag,
Pencil in hand and book upon the knee,
Will look and scribble, scribble on and look,
Until a man might travel twelve stout miles,
Or reap an acre of his neighbour's corn.
But, for that moping son of idleness,
Why can he tarry yonder?—In our churchyard
Is neither epitaph nor monument,
Tombstone nor name—only the turf we tread
And a few natural graves." To Jane, his wife,
Thus spake the homely priest of Ennerdale.
It was a July evening; and he sat
Upon the long stone-seat beneath the eaves,
Of his old cottage,—as it chanced, that day,
Employ'd in winter's work. Upon the stone
His wife sate near him, teasing matted wool,
While, from the twin cards tooth'd with glittering wire,
He fed the spindle of his youngest child,
Who turned her large round wheel in the open air
With back and forward steps. Towards the field
In which the parish chapel stood alone,
Girt round with a bare ring of mossy wall,
While half an hour went by, the priest had sent
Many a long look of wonder: and at last,
Risen from his seat, beside the snow-white ridge
Of carded wool which the old man had piled
He laid his implements with gentle care,
Each in the other lock'd; and, down the path
That from his cottage to the churchyard led,
He took his way, impatient to accost
The stranger, whom he saw still lingering there.

'Twas one well-known to him in former days,
A shepherd lad,—who, ere his sixteenth year,
Had left that calling, tempted to entrust
His expectations to the fickle winds
And perilous waters—with the mariners
A fellow-mariner—and so had fared
Through twenty seasons; but he had been rear'd
Among the mountains, and he in his heart
Was half a shepherd on the stormy seas.
Oft in the piping shrouds had Leonard heard
The tones of waterfalls and inland sounds
Of caves and trees:—and, when the regular wind
Between the tropics fill'd the steady sail,
And blew with the same breath through days and weeks,
Lengthening invisibly its weary line
Along the cloudless main, he, in those hours
Of tiresome indolence, would often hang
Over the vessel's side, and gaze and gaze;
And, while the broad green wave and sparkling foam
Flash'd round him images and hues that wrought
In union with the employment of his heart,
He, thus by feverish passion overcome,
Even with the organs of his bodily eye,
Below him, in the bosom of the deep,
Saw mountains—saw the forms of sheep that grazed
On verdant hills—with dwellings among trees,
And shepherds clad in the same country gray
Which he himself had worn.

And now at last
From perils manifold, with some small wealth
Acquired by traffic 'mid the Indian Isles,
To his paternal home he is return'd,
With a determined purpose to resume
The life he had lived there; both for the sake
Of many darling pleasures, and the love
Which to an only brother he has borne
In all his hardships, since that happy time
When, whether it blew foul or fair, they two
Were brother shepherds on their native hills.
—They were the last of all their race; and now,
When Leonard had approach'd his home, his heart

Fail'd in him; and, not venturing to inquire
Tidings of one whom he so dearly loved,
Towards the churchyard he had turn'd aside;
That as he knew in what particular spot
His family were laid, he thence might learn
If still his brother lived, or to the file
Another grave was added.—He had found
Another grave, near which a full half-hour
He had remain'd; but, as he gazed, there grew
Such a confusion in his memory,
That he began to doubt; and he had hopes
That he had seen this heap of turf before—
That it was not another grave, but one
He had forgotten. He had lost his path,
As up the vale, that afternoon, hewalk'd
Through fields which once had been well known to him:
And O what joy the recollection now
Sent to his heart! He lifted up his eyes,
And, looking round, imagined that he saw
Strange alteration wrought on every side
Among the woods and fields, and that the rocks
And everlasting hills themselves were changed.

By this the priest, who down the field had come
Unseen by Leonard, at the churchyard gate
Stopp'd short,—and thence, at leisure, limb by limb
Perused him with a gay complacency,
Ay, thought the vicar smiling to himself,
'Tis one of those who needs must leave the path
Of the world's business to go wild alone:
His arms have a perpetual holiday;
The happy man will creep about the fields,
Following his fancies by the hour, to bring
Tears down his cheek, or solitary smiles
Into his face, until the setting sun
Write Fool upon his forehead. Planted thus
Beneath a shed that over-arch'd the gate
Of this rude churchyard, till the stars appear'd,
The good man might have communed with himself,
But that the stranger, who had left the grave,
Approach'd; he recognised the priest at once,
And, after greetings interchanged, and given

By Leonard to the vicar as to one
Unknown to him, this dialogue ensued:

LEONARD.

You live, Sir, in these dales a quiet life;
Your years make up one peaceful family;
And who would grieve and fret, if, welcome come
And welcome gone, they are so like each other,
They cannot be remember'd? Scarce a funeral
Comes to this churchyard once in eighteen months;
And yet, some changes must take place among you;
And you, who dwell here, even among these rocks
Can trace the finger of mortality,
And see, that with our threescore years and ten
We are not all that perish.——I remember
(For many years ago I passed this road)
There was a foot-way all along the fields
By the brook-side—'tis gone—and that dark cleft!
To me it does not seem to wear the face
Which then it had.

PRIEST.

Nay, Sir, for aught I know,
That chasm is much the same—

LEONARD.

But, surely, yonder—

PRIEST.

Ay, there, indeed, your memory is a friend
That does not play you false.—On that tall pike
(It is the loneliest place of all these hills)
There were two springs that bubbled side by side,
As if they had been made that they might be
Companions for each other; the huge crag
Was rent with lightning—one hath disappear'd;
The other, left behind, is flowing still.[2]——
For accidents and changes such as these,
We want not store of them;—a waterspout
Will bring down half a mountain; what a feast
For folks that wander up and down like you,
To see an acre's breadth of that wide cliff
One roaring cataract!—a sharp May-storm

Will come with loads of January snow,
And in one night send twenty score of sheep
To feed the ravens: or a shepherd dies
By some untoward death among the rocks;
The ice breaks up and sweeps away a bridge—
A wood is fell'd:—and then for our own homes!
A child is born or christen'd, a field plough'd,
A daughter sent to service, a web spun,
The old house-clock is decked with a new face;
And hence, so far from wanting facts or dates
To chronicle the time, we all have here
A pair of diaries—one serving, Sir,
For the whole dale, and one for each fireside—
Yours was a stranger's judgment: for historians,
Commend me to these valleys!

LEONARD.

Yet your churchyard
Seems, if such freedom may be used with you,
To say that you are heedless of the past:
An orphan could not find his mother's grave:
Here's neither head nor foot-stone, plate of brass,
Cross-bones nor skull—type of our earthly state
Nor emblem of our hopes: the dead man's home
Is but a fellow to that pasture-field.

PRIEST.

Why, there, Sir, is a thought that's new to me!
The stone-cutters, 'tis true, might beg their bread
If every English churchyard were like ours;
Yet your conclusion wanders from the truth:
We have no need of names and epitaphs;
We talk about the dead by our firesides.
And then for our immortal part! we want
No symbols, Sir, to tell us that plain tale:
The thought of death sits easy on the man
Who has been born and dies among the mountains.

LEONARD.

Your dalesmen, then, do in each other's thoughts
Possess a kind of second life: no doubt
You, Sir, could help me to the history
Of half these graves?

PRIEST.

For eight-score winters past,
With what I've witness'd, and with what I've heard,
Perhaps I might; and on a winter-evening,
If you were seated at my chimney's nook,
By turning o'er these hillocks one by one,
We two could travel, Sir, through a strange round;
Yet all in the broad highway of the world.
Now there's a grave—your foot is half upon it—
It looks just like the rest; and yet that man
Died broken-hearted.

LEONARD.

'Tis a common case.
We'll take another: who is he that lies
Beneath yon ridge, the last of those three graves?
It touches on that piece of native rock
Left in the churchyard wall.

PRIEST.

That's Walter Ewbank.
He had as white a head and fresh a cheek
As ever were produced by youth and age
Engendering in the blood of hale fourscore.
Through five long generations had the heart
Of Walter's forefathers o'erflow'd the bounds
Of their inheritance, that single cottage—
You see it yonder!—and those few green fields.
They toil'd and wrought, and still, from sire to son,
Each struggled, and each yielded as before
A little—yet a little—and old Walter,
They left to him the family heart, and land
With other burthens than the crop it bore.
Year after year the old man still kept up
A cheerful mind, and buffeted with bond,
Interest, and mortgages; at last he sank,
And went into his grave before his time.
Poor Walter! whether it was care that spurred him
God only knows, but to the very last
He had the lightest foot in Ennerdale:
His pace was never that of an old man:
I almost see him tripping down the path

With his two grandsons after him;—but you,
Unless our landlord be your host to-night,
Have far to travel—and on these rough paths
Even in the longest day of midsummer—

LEONARD.

But those two orphans!

PRIEST.

Orphans!—such they were—
Yet not while Walter lived:—for, though their parents
Lay buried side by side as now they lie,
The old man was a father to the boys,
Two fathers in one father:—and if tears,
Shed when he talk'd of them where they were not,
And hauntings from the infirmity of love,
Are aught of what makes up a mother's heart,
This old man, in the day of his old age,
Was half a mother to them.—If you weep, Sir,
To hear a stranger talking about strangers,
Heaven bless you when you are among your kindred!
Ay—you may turn that way—it is a grave
Which will bear looking at.

LEONARD.

These boys—I hope
They loved this good old man?—

PRIEST.

They did—and truly:
But that was what we almost overlook'd,
They were such darlings of each other. For,
Though from their cradles they had lived with Walter,
The only kinsman near them, and though he
Inclined to them, by reason of his age,
With a more fond, familiar tenderness,
They, notwithstanding, had much love to spare,
And it all went into each other's hearts.
Leonard, the elder by just eighteen months,
Was two years taller; 'twas a joy to see,
To hear, to meet them!—From their house the school
Is distant three short miles—and in the time
Of storm and thaw, when every water-course

And unbridged stream, such as you may have noticed
Crossing our roads at every hundred steps,
Was swoln into a noisy rivulet,
Would Leonard then, when elder boys perhaps
Remain'd at home, go staggering through the fords,
Bearing his brother on his back. I've seen him
On windy days, in one of those stray brooks—
Ay, more than once I've seen him—mid-leg deep,
Their two books lying both on a dry stone
Upon the hither side; and once I said,
As I remember, looking round these rocks
And hills on which we all of us wereborn,
That God who made the great book of the world
Would bless such piety—

LEONARD.

It may be then—

PRIEST.

Never did worthier lads break English bread;
The finest Sunday that the autumn saw
With all its mealy clusters of ripenuts,
Could never keep these boys away from church,
Or tempt them to an hour of Sabbath breach.
Leonard and James! I warrant, every corner
Among these rocks, and every hollow place
Where foot could come, to one or both of them
Was known as well as to the flowers that grow there.
Like roe-bucks they went bounding o'er the hills;
They played like two young ravens on the crags;
Then they could write, ay, and speak too as well
As many of their betters—and for Leonard!
The very night before he went away,
In my own house I put into his hand
A Bible, and I'd wager house and field
That, if he is alive, he has it yet.

LEONARD.

It seems, these brothers have not lived to be
A comfort to each other—

PRIEST.

That they might

Live to such end, is what both old and young
In this our valley all of us have wish'd,
And what, for my part, I have often pray'd:
But Leonard—

LEONARD.

Then James is still left among you?

PRIEST.

'Tis of the elder brother I am speaking:
They had an uncle:—he was at that time
A thriving man, and traffick'd on the seas;
And, but for that same uncle, to this hour
Leonard had never handled rope or shroud.
For the boy loved the life which we lead here:
And though of unripe years, a stripling only,
His soul was knit to this his native soil.
But, as I said, old Walter was too weak
To strive with such a torrent; when he died,
The estate and house were sold; and all their sheep,
A pretty flock, and which, for aught I know,
Had clothed the Ewbanks for a thousand years:—
Well—all was gone, and they were destitute.
And Leonard, chiefly for his brother's sake,
Resolved to try his fortune on the seas.
Twelve years are past since we had tidings from him.
If there were one among us who had heard
That Leonard Ewbank was come home again,
From the great Gavel,[3] down by Leeza's banks,
And down the Enna, far as Egremont,
The day would be a very festival;
And those two bells of ours, which there you see
Hanging in the open air—but, O, good Sir!
This is sad talk—they'll never sound for him—
Living or dead. When last we heard of him,
He was in slavery among the Moors
Upon the Barbary coast. 'Twas not a little
That would bring down his spirit; and no doubt,
Before it ended in his death, the youth
Was sadly cross'd—Poor Leonard! when we parted,
He took me by the hand, and said to me,
If ever the day came when he was rich,

He would return, and on his father's land
He would grow old among us.

LEONARD.

If that day
Should come, 'twould needs be a glad day for him;
He would himself, no doubt, be happy then
As any that should meet him—

PRIEST.

Happy! Sir—

LEONARD.

You said his kindred all were in their graves,
And that he had one brother—

PRIEST.

That is but
A fellow tale of sorrow. From his youth
James, though not sickly, yet was delicate;
And Leonard being always by his side
Had done so many offices about him,
That, though he was not of a timid nature,
Yet still the spirit of a mountain boy
In him was somewhat check'd; and, when his brother
Was gone to sea, and he was left alone,
The little colour that he had was soon
stolen from his cheek; he droop'd, and pined, and pined—

LEONARD.

But these are all the graves of full-grown men!

PRIEST.

Ay, Sir, that pass'd away: we took him to us;
He was the child of all the dale—he lived
Three months with one, and six months with another;
And wanted neither food, nor clothes, nor love;
And many, many happy days were his.
But, whether blithe or sad, 'tis my belief
His absent brother still was at his heart.
And, when he dwelt beneath our roof, we found
(A practice till this time unknown to him)
That often, rising from his bed at night,
He in his sleep would walk about, and sleeping

He sought his brother Leonard.—You are moved;
Forgive me, Sir: before I spoke to you,
I judged you most unkindly.

LEONARD.

But this youth
How did he die at last?

PRIEST.

One sweet May morning
(It will be twelve years since when Spring returns)
He had gone forth among the new-dropp'd lambs,
With two or three companions, whom their course
Of occupation led from height to height
Under a cloudless sun, till he, at length,
Through weariness, or, haply, to indulge
The humour of the moment, lagg'd behind.
You see yon precipice;—it wears the shape
Of a vast building made of many crags;
And in the midst is one particular rock
That rises like a column from the vale,
Whence by our shepherds it is called The Pillar.
Upon its aëry summit crown'd with heath,
The loiterer, not unnoticed by his comrades,
Lay stretch'd at ease; but, passing by the place
On their return, they found that he was gone.
No ill was fear'd; but one of them by chance
Entering, when evening was far spent, the house
Which at that time was James's home, there learned
That nobody had seen him all that day;
The morning came, and still he was unheard of;
The neighbours were alarm'd, and to the brook
Some hasten'd, some towards the lake; ere noon
They found him at the foot of that same rock—
Dead, and with mangled limbs. The third day after
I buried him, poor youth, and there he lies!

LEONARD.

And that then is his grave!—Before his death
You say that he saw many happy years?

PRIEST.

Ay, that he did—

LEONARD.

And all went well with him?—

PRIEST.

If he had one, the youth had twenty homes.

LEONARD.

And you believe, then, that his mind was easy?

PRIEST.

Yes, long before he died, he found that time
Is a true friend to sorrow; and unless
His thoughts were turn'd on Leonard's luckless fortune,
He talk'd about him with a cheerful love.

LEONARD.

He could not come to an unhallow'd end!

PRIEST.

Nay, God forbid!—You recollect I mention'd
A habit which disquietude and grief
Had brought upon him; and we all conjectured
That, as the day was warm, he had lain down
Upon the grass, and waiting for his comrades,
He there had fallen asleep; that in his sleep
He to the margin of the precipice
Had walk'd, and from the summit had fallen headlong.
And so, no doubt, he perished: at the time,
We guess, that in his hands he must have held
His shepherd's staff: for midway in the cliff
It had been caught; and there for many years
It hung, and moulder'd there.

The priest here ended—
The stranger would have thank'd him, but he felt
A gushing from his heart, that took away
The power of speech. Both left the spot in silence;
And Leonard, when they reach'd the churchyard gate,
As the priest lifted up the latch, turned round,
And, looking at the grave, he said, "My Brother!"
The vicar did not hear the words: and now,
Pointing towards the cottage, he entreated
That Leonard would partake his homely fare;
The other thank'd him with a fervent voice,

But added, that, the evening being calm,
He would pursue his journey. So they parted.
It was not long ere Leonard reach'd a grove
That overhung the road: he there stopp'd short,
And, sitting down beneath the trees, review'd
All that the priest had said: his early years
Were with him in his heart: his cherish'd hopes,
And thoughts which had been his an hour before,
All press'd on him with such a weight, that now
This vale, where he had been so happy, seem'd
A place in which he could not bear to live:
So he relinquish'd all his purposes.
He travell'd on to Egremont: and thence,
That night, he wrote a letter to the priest,
Reminding him of what had pass'd between them;
And adding, with a hope to be forgiven,
That it was from the weakness of his heart
He had not dared to tell him who he was.

This done, he went on shipboard, and is now
A seaman, a grey-headed mariner.

EMMA; OR, THE MURDERED MAID.

A TRAGEDY OF THE LAKE DISTRICT.

ON the death of Emma's father, she found herself, with a widowed mother, deprived, at one stroke, of nearly all the comforts, and the means ofprocuring them, which she had enjoyed during her father's lifetime. A small jointure of thirty pounds a-year was all that remained to her mother, for her father had died insolvent.

This thirty pounds a-year Emma thought might support her mother, if she could support herself. Determined to burden no one for her subsistence, and believing that humble servitude was, in the eyes of Heaven and of men, more honourable than a mean and degrading dependence on the bounty of friends for a precarious supply of our temporary wants.

Her mother strenuously opposed Emma's resolution of going to service. She would subject herself to any privations, rather than her young and lovely daughter would be reduced to this severe necessity—she would work for hire —she would beg—she would borrow—she should almost steal, rather than Emma should be compelled to labour. Her mother's entreaties, however, so far from having the desired effect of preventing her going to service, only confirmed Emma in her previous resolution. Should she be a burden to her mother—to that mother who expressed so tender a solicitation for herwelfare —who was rapidly descending the downhill of life—who had all her days been accustomed to the elegances of taste? No, no; rather than take anything from her, she would add a little to her comforts; and a portion of her yearly wage should be set apart as a present to her mother.

The affectionate mother, who had never before parted a single day with her daughter, saw her set out to her place of service (a gentleman's family among the lakes, where her father had been upon terms of intimacy) with an aching heart. She felt as if she was parting with her for the last time; and required all the resolution she was mistress of to tear herself from her dear Emma. "Go," she said, "and take a mother's fondest, warmest blessing; and if you should find yourself unable to accomplish your resolution, or feel any inconvenience, return and share what Heaven has left us, with an affectionate mother. It is not much, Heaven knows; but I could doubly enjoy it, were it less, if I had you to share it." Emma assured her mother, that if any unforeseen difficulty occurred, she would instantly repair to her natal home; and cheered her witha promise of constantly writing. This pacified, but did not console her mother. She knew too well the independent spirit of her daughter to hope for her return, except on some awful emergency.

Time rolled on, and repeated letters, both from Emma and her mistress, assured the mother that all was well, and that Emma was healthy and happy. At length Emma sent the joyful intelligence that she would come over on Whitsun Sunday morning, and spend the week with her.

Emma arose, with buoyant spirits, packed up a small bundle of necessaries in a handkerchief, put her wages in her bosom, and set out to see and cheer her affectionate parent. The morning was extremely fine, and she amused herself with the bright and varied prospect, till the road, descending a steep hill, led her into a richly romantic valley. A copse of wood overhung the road, a huge rock formed the fence on that side next the wood, and seemed like a natural wall. Over the rock fell, in three or four unequal cascades, the stream of a brook which might be heard tumbling through the wood to a considerable distance. Close to the place where the water left the wood, one part of the rock shot up to an immense height, bearing no very distant resemblance to the ruins of an old castle. From a fissure in the rock grew the stump of an old oak, whose branches had apparently been lopped by the wind, except one, which, bending down almost to the stream, had escaped its ravages by its humble situation. On a large stone, in this romantic spot, Emma sat down to rest herself awhile, and slake her thirst at the stream.

Though Emma's heart did not entertain a thought but of the joy her mother would feel on receiving the first-fruits of her first wages, every bosom was not warmed by so generous an impulse. Sam the cow-lad at Emma's master's had ascertained that she had that day received her wages, and was gone to her mother's; and he instantly formed the resolution to rob the generous girl of the hard earned pittance. By a nearer route, over the hills, he sought to meet her in this solitary spot, where there was little possibility of being surprised in the action. While Emma was thus meditating on the happiness which she would soon feel in her mother's arms, Sam came up and commanded her to deliver up her money; she entreated him to leave her a little for a present to her mother, but the human fiend (and human fiends are the worst fiends), refused to leave her a farthing. He had secured the booty, and Emma was preparing to pursue her journey, when the horrid thought entered his head, that unless he added murder to his robbery, he would be liable to punishment for his crime. There was not a moment for deliberation; and the lovely, the young, the innocent Emma fell a corpse at the wretch's feet. Fear added wings to the speed of the villain, and he fled, as if from the face ofheaven.

The day passed on with the same calm serenity as if nothing had happened. Noon came to the widow's cottage but no Emma arrived. As the evening drew on the mother's unhappiness increased; and she set out to meet her daughter, for whose fate she felt most keenly, without being able to assign any cause. As the sun was sinking, amid a rich profusion of evening tints, which threw a dazzling lustre over all the scene, the widow reached the vale where her murdered daughter slept her last long sleep. But the pencil alone can finish the picture—words are of no utility.

It would be superfluous to say that I would have the last picture sketched at the moment when the mother first discovers that it is the lifeless body of her daughter that lies stained with its own gore, that she is bending over. Cold must be that heart that would not feel the full force of such a piece. Poor would the richest landscape you ever drew appear, when compared with this.

It is strange that those who profess to have hearts so open to the beauties of nature, should reject the loveliest object in it. Adam, though placed in the midst of Paradise, was not content till Eve was added to its other beauties; nor would I ever draw a picture without such an enlivening object. Beside, in most of our fine sublime scenes about the lakes, we lose the principal zest of the piece by having nothing beautiful to contrast with the rugged. The more wild and terrible the scene I had to paint, the greater care would I take to introduce some lovely female form to mark the contrast; then

“Each would give each a double charm,
Like pearls upon an Ethiop’s arm.”

HISTORICAL, POETICAL, AND ROMANTIC

ASSOCIATIONS OF CARLISLE.

NO one versed in ballad lore—no reader of old poetry and romance, can approach Carlisle for the first time without pleasurable emotion. Carlisle is the border city—the city of King Arthur and his knights. It has been the scene of many a stout siege and bloody feud; of many a fierce foray, and mournful execution, and of many a just punishment upon traitors and reivers. It is, consequently, not to be pictured to the imagination without unusual interest. Old traditions of events like these have made it among the most remarkable of the cities of England; and it would be difficult to name another around which are clustered so many memories of such various degrees of attraction to the poetical and historical antiquary. Its approach from the south, though striking, gives no idea of its antiquity and former feudalism. It is situated in an extensive plain, surrounded in the distance by mountains, amongst which Saddleback, Skiddaw, and Crossfell, are prominent; and from afar off, with the smoke of its households hanging over it, does undoubtedly impress the imagination with ideas of the romantic.

Nearer approach, however, dissipates this illusion. We lose sight of the valley, being in it, and of the mountains, in the presence of immediate objects. Tall chimneys rear their heads in considerable numbers, pouring forth steam and smoke, and with square buildings and their numerous windows, prove incontestably that modern Carlisle is a manufacturing city, and has associations very different from those of its former history. On entrance, the contrast between the past and the present becomes still more vivid. We see that its walls and gates have disappeared; that its streets are clean, wide and comfortable, which no ancient streets in England ever were; and that it has altogether a juvenile, busy, and thriving appearance, giving few signs (to the eye at least) that it has been in existence above a century. It is true that two venerable relics, its castle and its cathedral, remain to attest its bygone grandeur and glory; but these are not immediately visible, and have to be sought out by the enquiring stranger; whilst all around him is modern and prosaic; and a mere reduplication of the same characteristics of English life and manners that he must have seen in a hundred other places.

Still, however, it is "merry Carlisle," and "bonnie Carlisle," although, like all other mundane things, it has been changed by time; and is quite as much King Arthur's city as England is King Arthur's England; and brimfull of associations which the traveller will be at no loss to recall, of the crime and sorrow—the "fierce wars and faithful loves" of our ancestors, from the year 800 downwards to 1745. Not that Carlisle is only a thousand years old. It has a much earlier origin than the year 800, having been founded by the Romans. By them it was called Luguballium, or Luguvallum, signifying the tower or station by the wall, and was so named from its contiguity to the wall of Severus. The Saxons, disliking this long and awkward name, abbreviated it into Luel; and afterwards in speaking of it, called it Caer-luel, or the city of Luel; from whence comes its present designation of Carlisle. It is supposed to have been during the Saxon period, if not the chief city, the frequent residence of that great mythic personage, King Arthur, where he

With fifty good and able
Knights that resorted unto him
And were of his round table:
Did hold his jousts and tournaments,
Whereto were many pressed,
Wherein some knights did far excel
And eke surmount the rest.

Among these knights, Sir Lancelot du Lake, Sir Bevis, and Sir Gawaine are the most conspicuous in tradition. One of the most celebrated of our most ancient ballads relates to the latter, and to his marriage with the mis-shapen lady that afterwards became so fair. The story is a very beautiful one; and was the model upon which Chaucer founded his Wife of Bath's Tale. It is worth repeating, for the sake of those to whom the uncouth rhymes of ancient days are not familiar; but though it is likely enough that the number of these is but few, it is too interesting, as connected with Carlisle, to be left unmentioned in a chapter expressly devoted to the poetical antiquities of the place.

THE MARRIAGE OF SIR GAWAINE.

King Arthur lives in merry Carleile,
And seemly is to see:
And there with him queene Guenever,
That bride so bright of blee.

And there with him queene Guenever,
That bride so bright in bowre;
And all his barons about him stoode,
That were both stiffe and stowre.

The king a royale Christmasse kept,
With mirth and princelye cheare;

To him repaired many a knighte,
That came both farre and neare.

And when they were to dinner sette,
And cups went freely round:
Before them came a faire damsèlle,
And knelt upon the ground.

Aboone! a boone! O kinge Arthùre,
I beg a boone of thee;
Avenge me of a carlish knighte,
Who hath shent my love and me.

At Tearne-Wadling,[4] his castle stands,
Near to that lake so fair,
And proudlye rise the battlements,
And streamers deck the air.

Noe gentle knighte, nor ladye gay,
May pass that castle-walle;
But from that foule discurteous knighte,
Mishappe will them befalle.

Hee's twyce the size of common men,
Wi' thewes, and sinewes stronge,
And on his backe he bears a clubbe,
That is both thicke and longe.

This grimme baròne, 'twas our harde happe,
But yester morne to see;
When to his bowre he bare my love,
And sore misused me.

And when I told him, King Arthùre
As lyttle shold him spare;
Goe tell, sayd he, that cuckold kinge,
To meete me if he dare.

Upp then sterted King Arthùre,
And sware by hille and dale,
He ne'er wolde quitt that grimme baròne,
Till he had made him quail.

King Arthur sets off in a great rage. The opprobrious term, which galled him the more because it was true, fired his blood, and he challenged the "grimme baròne" to mortal combat.

Sir Gawaine, who seems to have been of a stature as gigantic as the famous Sir Hugh Cæsar, who is buried at Penrith, conquered him by enchantment: his sinews lost their strength, his arms sank powerless at his side; and he only received the boon of life at the hands of his enemy by swearing upon his faith as a knight, to return upon New Year's day, and bring "true word what thing it was that women most desired."

Go fetch my sword Excalibar:
Goe saddle mee my steede,
Nowe, by my faye, that grimme baròne
Shall rue this ruthfulle deede.

And when he came to Tearne-Wadling,
Beneath the castle-walle;
"Come forth; come forth; thou proud baròne,
Or yielde thyself my thralle."

On magicke grounde that castle stoode,
And fenc'd with many a spelle:
Noe valiant knighte could tread thereon,
But straite his courage felle.

Forth then rush'd that carlish knight,
King Arthur felte the charme:
His sturdy sinews lost their strengthe,
Down sunke his feeble arme.

Nowe yield thee, yield thee, King Arthùre,
Nowe yield thee unto mee:
Or fighte with mee, or lose thy lande,
Noe better terms maye bee.

Unlesse thou sweare upon the rood,
And promise on thy faye,
Here to returne to Tearne-Wadling
Upon the New Yeare's daye:

And bringe me worde what thing it is
All women moste desyre:
This is thy ransome, Arthùre, he says,
Ile have noe other hyre.

King Arthur then helde up his hande,
And sweare upon his faye,
Then tooke his leave of the grimme baròne,
And faste hee rode awaye.

And he rode east, and he rode west,
And did of all inquyre,
What thing it is all women crave,
And what they most desyre.

King Arthur made due inquiry; but it was not so easy a matter to discover the secret.

Some told him riches, pompe, or state;
Some rayment fine and brighte;
Some told him mirthe; some flatterye;
And some a jollye knighte:

In letters all King Arthur wrote,
And seal'd them with his ringe;
But still his minde was helde in doubte,
Each tolde a different thinge.

As New Year's day approached, his tribulation increased; for though he might have told the "grimme baròne" with much truth many things that women did much desire, he was not at all sure that his version of what they most desired, would hit the fancy of the Lord of Tarn-Wadling, who had set him to expound the riddle. He would not give up, however, and one day,—

As ruthfulle he rode over a more,
He saw a ladye sitte
Between an oke, and a greene holléye,
All clad in "red scarlette."

Her nose was crookt and turned outwàrde,
Her chin stoode all awreye;
And where as sholde have been her mouthe,
Lo! there was set her eye:

Her haires, like serpents, clung aboute
Her cheekes of deadlye hewe:
A worse-form'd ladye than she was,
No man mote ever viewe.

This ill-conditioned damsel tells him the secret, however, upon condition that he will bring her a "fair and courtly knight to marry her,"—a condition which, considering all the circumstances, must have seemed to the good king as bad as the jumping out of the frying-pan into the fire. The great secret is, as she expresses it, "that all women will have their wille, and this is their chief desyre," which Arthur forthwith tells to the "grimme baròne;" and so acquits himself as far as he is concerned. The other trouble, however, still remains, and fills the king's mind with anxiety. Queen Guinevere, who was outraged as well as her husband by the opprobrious message of the "grimme baròne," but who had never thought of the very obvious solution of the riddle he had been set, comes out to meet him on his return, and inquires how he has sped. He details his new tribulation in having promised to procure a fair knight to marry this ugly, mis-shapen creature. Comfort is nearer at hand than he thought, and Sir Gawaine, his own nephew, "his sister's son," bids him "be merrye and lighte," for he will marry her, however foul and loathsome she may be. He does so accordingly:—

And when they were in wed-bed laid,
  And all were done awaye:
"Come turne to me, mine owne wed-lord,
  Come turne to mee, I praye."

Sir Gawaine scant could lift his head,
  For sorrowe and for care;
When lo! instead of that lothelye dame,
  He sawe a young ladye faire.

Sweet blushes stayn'd her rud-red cheeke,
  Her eyen were blacke as sloe;
The ripening cherrye swellde her lippe,
  And all her necke was snowe.

Agreeably surprised at the change, Sir Gawaine soon learns to love the lady. She informs him that, by a cruel fate, she cannot be fair both night and day; and asks him which he prefers. He hints that the night would be most pleasant; to which she replies:—

What when gaye ladyes goe with their lordes
  To drinke the ale and wine;
Alas! then I must hide myself,
  I must not go, with mine?

"My faire ladyè, Sir Gawaine sayd,
  I yield me to thy skille;
Because thou art my owne ladye
  Thou shalt have all thy wille."

The spell is broken. She tells him her history; and that henceforth she shall be fair both night and day.

My father was an aged knighte,
  And yet it chanced soe,
He took to wife a false ladyè,

Whiche broughte me to this woe.

Shee witch'd mee, being a faire younge maide,
In the grene forèst to dwelle;
And there to abide in lothlye shape,
Most like a fiend of helle.

Midst mores and mosses, woods, and wilds;
To lead a lonesome life:
Till some yonge faire and courtlye knighte
Wolde marrye me for his wife:

Nor fully to game mine owne trewe shape,
Such was her devilish skille;
Until he wolde yielde to be ruled by mee,
And let mee have all my wille.

She witch'd my brother to a carlish boore,
And made him stiffe and stronge;
And built him a bowre on magicke grounde,
To live by rapine and wronge.

But now the spelle is broken throughe,
And wronge is turnde to righte;
Henceforth I shall bee a faire ladyè,
And hee a gentle knighte.

Another ballad, equally celebrated, though not so beautiful, also relates to King Arthur's residence at Carlisle, and to the truth of the imputation cast upon Queen Guinevere by the "grimme baròne" of the last story. It is entitled "The Boy and the Mantle," commencing somewhat uncouthly:—

In the third day of May,
To Carleile did come
A kind curteous child
That cold much of wisdome.

This "child" brings that wondrous mantle which no lady who is not chaste can wear; and it is tried upon all the dames of the court. When Queen Guinevere put it on, it was suddenly rent from the top to the bottom, and turned in succession all manner of colours, and is told as follows:—

God speed thee, king Arthur,
Sitting at thy meate;
And the goodly queene Guinevere,
I cannott her forgett.

I tell you, lords, in this hall;
  I bid you all to "heede;"
Except you be the more surer
  Is you for to dread.

He plucked out of his "porterner,"
  And longer wold not dwell,
He pulled forth a pretty mantle,
  Betweene two nut-shells.

Have thou here, king Arthur;
  Have thou here of mee,
Give itt to thy comely queene
  Shapen as itt is alreadye.

Itt shall never become that wiffe,
  That hath once done amisse.
Then every knight in the king's court
  Began to care for "his."

Forth came dame Guinevere;
  To the mantle shee her "hied;"
The ladye shee was newfangle,
  But yett she was affrayd.

When she had taken the mantle;
  She stoode as shee had beene madd;
It was from the top to the toe
  As sheeres had itt shread.

One while was it "gule;"
  Another while was itt greene;
Another while was it wadded:
  Ill itt did her beseeme.

Another while was it blacke
  And bore the worst hue:
By my troth, quoth king Arthur,
  I thinke thou be not true.

She threw down the mantle,
  That bright was of blee;
Fast, with a rudd redd,
  To her chamber can shee flee.

She curst the weaver, and the walker
  That clothe that had wrought;

And bade a vengeance on his crowne,
That hither had it broughte.

The lady of Sir Kay, another of King Arthur's knights, tries it on with no better success; and the ballad thus corroborates the old traditions reported by the earliest historians, that the court of the British King was anything but a pure one, "and that Queen Guinevere was noted for breach of faith to her husband," especially with her husband's friend, Sir Lancelot du Lake, the hero himself of many a goodly ballad; and of some passages in the Morte Arthur.

Mixing the real with the fabulous history of Carlisle, and taking both in chronological order, we must leave these ancient ballads to relate that, during the period of the British Kings, Carlisle suffered from the incursions of the Scots and Picts, by whom it was ultimately reduced to ruins; it was rebuilt by Egfrid, King of Northumberland, who surrounded and fortified it with a wall; founded a monastery and a college of secular priests. It was once more destroyed by the Danes, about the year 900, who threw down the walls, burned its houses, chiefly built of wood, and killed every person in it, man, woman, and child. It remained in ruins, it is believed, for nearly 200 years. On the return of William Rufus from Alnwick, after concluding a peace with the turbulent Scotch, he passed over the remains of this once celebrated city, and observing that it must have been a place of great strength, and could be made so again, he resolved to rebuild it for the protection of the border. He did so: and Carlisle became of more importance than it had ever been before. Its castle was built and garrisoned; and every means taken to render it a stronghold both for offensive and defensive warfare. Henry the First completed what Rufus had so well begun, erected Carlisle into an Episcopal see in the year 1132, making Athelwold, his confessor, the firstbishop.

In Evans's Collection of Old Ballads is one relating to a bishop of Carlisle at this early period. It is entitled "Bishop Thurston and the King of Scots," and contains some beautiful passages which render it worthy of all the publicity that can be given to it; especially as the whole composition inculcates sentiments of abhorrence for warfare, rare at the time it was penned, but now, happily, in the ascendant. Soon after King Stephen's departure for Normandy, A.D. 1137, the King of Scotland entered England in a hostile manner. Stephen's Government was not in a position to resist an invasion at that time; and the miseries of war were averted by the interposition of the venerable Bishop Thurston, who prevailed upon the Scotch King to meet him at Roxburgh, and used such arguments as induced him to return to his own country in peace. They are said to have been arguments of Christian charity, and not the arguments of policy and the sword, which bishops as well as barons could use in those days. A few stanzas will show the excellent spirit of the ballad.

Through the fair country of Tiviotdale
King David marched forth;
King David and his princely son,
The heroes of the North.

And holy Thurston fro' merry Carlisle,
In haste his way doth wind,
With many a cross-bearer before,
And many a knight behind.

The arguments used by the bishop to dissuade the invader are of universal interest, and as applicable now as then:—

Out then spoke the holy Thurston,
And full of woe spake he,
"O Christ, thy kingdom of heavenly bliss,
Alas, when shall we see!

For here on earth is nought but sin,
And kings for pride do ill,
And when they with each other war
The poor folks blood must spill.

What hath the husbandman done wrong
That he must spoil his grain?
What the poor widow, and what the child,
That they must all be slain?

And what is the simple maid to blame
To be made of lust the prey?
And what the lowly village priest
That they so oft do slay?

And when the doleful day of doom
Shall call ye from the grave,
From the crying blood of these innocents
What tyrants shall ye save?

Now think thee well, O mortal King,
And thy misdeeds bemoan,
And think what will save thy hapless soul,
When all thy pomp is gone.

Nor fancy that alms will save thy soul,

Though bounteous they be given;
Nor the rearing of abbeys all rich endowed
Will carry thy soul to heaven."

From the time of Henry I. the place began to prosper, though it appears from Stowe that, in 1829, a great portion of it was burned down. In the year 1300, King Edward I. summoned his barons and knights to meet him here on the feast-day of St. John the Baptist, to prepare for the invasion of Scotland; which was afterwards commenced by the siege of Carlaverock castle. The same monarch also summoned a Parliament to meet here in the year 1307, the last parliament of his reign. A complete list of the members who attended is to be found in Stowe's *Annals*, including, says the historian, "eighty-seven earls and barons, twenty bishops, sixty-one abbots, and eight priors, besides many deacons, archdeacons and other inferior clerks. The subject of their deliberations was the Scottish war, and the sore annoyance given by Robert Bruce. The King remained here from January, when the Parliament was summoned, during all the winter and summer, disposing of many things concerning Scotland at his pleasure," but vexing himself to death at his inability, from sickness and other causes, to march against Robert Bruce. He had some revenge, however, for a party of his men "capturing one Thomas, that was a knight, and one Alexander, that was a priest and dean ofGlasgow," who had been sent by Robert Bruce to "allure away the English people by gentle persuasion;" he had them summarily hanged, drawn, and quartered, and placed their heads upon the gates of Carlisle—those gates where the heads of so many Scotchmen were afterwards to grin in ghastly horror until 1745.

Among the poetical and historical associations connected with Carlisle, the famous battle of Otterbourne, and the still more famous ballad which celebrates it, must not be omitted. In the twelfth year of Richard II., A.D. 1388, the Scotch made a great raid over the border, and ravaged the whole country about Carlisle, driving away large quantities of cattle, and taking no less than 300 men prisoners. Another division of them extended their ravages into the counties of Northumberland and Durham; and grew so insolent as to render a vigorous effort necessary to crush them, on the part of the English.

It fell about the Lammas tide
When yoemen win their hay,
The doughty Douglass 'gan to ride
In England to take a prey.

The Earl of Fife withoute strife
He bound him over Solway.
The great wolde even together ride

The race they may rue for aye.

The version of the ballad, as given by Percy, is the only one of the many versions extant which makes allusion to the party that ravaged Carlisle. The main interest is centred around Newcastle, and on the doings of the other division of the Scotch. There is, however, another ballad of which Carlisle is more exclusively the theme. It is somewhat less known to the English reader, not being found in Percy's *Reliques*; and describes a scene which was very common to the border for a long period. Mr. Gilbert has illustrated it by a picturesque sketch. The principal portions of this ballad, sufficient to tell the story, are here transcribed. In the year 1596, William Armstrong, of Kinmont, better known as Kinmont Willie, a noted reiver, or border trooper, and stealer of Englishmen's cattle, was taken prisoner by Lord Scrope, the Warden of the Western Marches, and safely lodged in Carlisle Castle. A truce existed at the time between Lord Scrope and the Lord of Buccleugh, who severally watched over the interests of the English and Scottish sides of the border; and the Lord of Buccleugh, incensed that the truce had been broken by the capture of Willie, demanded that he should be set at liberty. Lord Scrope refused; and the Lord of Buccleugh, with a small body of two hundred men, performed the daring feat of surprising the castle of Carlisle, and rescuing his countryman. The "fause Sakelde," alluded to in the ballad, was the then possessor of Corby castle, and sheriff of Cumberland—the chief of the powerful family of the Salkeldes; and "Hairibee" was the slang phrase for the place of execution at Carlisle.

KINMONT WILLIE.

O have ye na heard o' the fause Sakelde,
  O have ye na heard o' the keen Lord Scrope,
How they have taken bold Kinmont Willie
  On Hairibee to hang him up?

Had Willie had but twenty men—
  But twenty men as stout as he,
Fause Sakelde had never the Kinmont ta'en
  Wi' eight score in his company.

They bound his legs beneath the steed,
  They tied his hands behind his back,
They guarded him, five score on each side,
  And brought him over the Liddel-rack.

They led him through the Liddel-rack,

And also through the Carlisle sands,
They brought him to Carlisle Castell
To be at my Lord Scrope's commands.

Now word is gone to the bold keeper
In Branksome hall where that he lay,
That Lord Scrope had taken Kinmont Willie
Between the hours of night and day.

He struck the table with his hand,
He made the red wine spring on hie—
"Now Christ's curse on my head," he said,
"But avenged on Lord Scrope I will be.

"O is my helmet a widow's cap,
Or my lance a wand of the willow tree?
Or my arm a lady's lily hand,
That an English Lord should lightly me?

"And have they taken him, Kinmont Willie,
Against the truce of Border tide?
And forgotten that the bold Buccleugh
Is keeper here on the Scottish side?

"And have they taken him, Kinmont Willie,
Withouten either dread or fear,
And forgotten that the bold Buccleugh,
Can back a steed and shake a spear?

"O were there war between the lands,
As well as I wot that there is none,
I would slight Carlisle Castell high,
Though it were builded of marble stone.

"I would set that Castell in a low,
And sloken it with English blood,
There's never a man in Cumberland
Should tell where Carlisle Castell stood.

"But since nae war's between the lands
And there is peace and peace should be;
I'll neither harm English lad or lass,
And yet the Kinmont shall go free."

Then on we held for Carlisle town
And at Staneshaw bank the Eden we crossed,
The water was great and mickle of spait

But there never a man nor horse we lost.

And when we reached the Staneshaw bank,
The wind was rising loud and hie,
And there the laird gar'd leave our steeds
For fear that they should stamp and nie.

And when we left the Staneshaw bank,
The wind began full loud to blaw,
But 'twas wind and weet, and fire and sleet,
When we came beneath the castle wa'.

We crept on knees and held our breath,
Till we placed the ladders against the wa',
And ready was bold Buccleugh himself
To mount the first before us a'.

He has ta'en the watchman by the throat,
He flung him down upon the lead;
"Had there not been peace between our land,
Upon the other side thou hadst gaed."

"Now sound our trumpet," quoth Buccleugh,
Let's waken Lord Scrope, right merrilie;
Then loud the Warder's trumpet blew,
"Wha daur meddle wi' me?"

Wi' coulters and wi' forehammers
We garred the bars bang merrilie,
Until we came to the inner prison,
Where Kinmont Willie he did lie.

And when we came to the lower prison,
Where Kinmont Willie he did lie.
"O sleep ye, wake ye, Kinmont Willie,
Upon the morn that thou's to die?"

"O, I sleep saft, and I wake aft,
It's long since sleeping was fley'd frae me!
Gie my service back to my wife and bairns,
And a' gude fellows that speir for me!"

The Red Rowan has lifted him up
The starkest man in Teviotdale;
"Abide, abide now, Red Rowan,
Till of Lord Scrope I take farewell.

"Farewell, farewell, my good Lord Scrope,
My good Lord Scrope, farewell," he cried,
"I'll pay you for my lodging maill,
When first we meet on the border side."

Then shoulder high, with shout and cry,
We bore him down the ladder lang,
At every stride Red Rowan made
I wot the Kinmont's airms played clang.

"O, mony a time," quoth Kinmont Willie,
"I have ridden horse both wild andwoad,
But a rougher beast than Red Rowan,
I ween my legs have ne'erbestrode!"

We scarce had reached the Haneshawbank,
When all the Carlisle hills were rung,
And a thousand men on horse and foot
Came wi' the keen Lord Scrope along.

Buccleugh has turned to Eden water,
Even where it flowed from bank tobrim,
And he has plunged in wi' a' his band
And safely swam them thro' the stream.

He turned him on the other side,
And at Lord Scrope his glove flung he,
"If ye like na' my visit in merry England,
In fair Scotland come visitme!"

This was a daring exploit, and has been gallantly sung. The words seem to come out of the mouth of one of the very moss troopers who had acted a part in the achievement, and the whole composition is rough but finely flavoured; and strongly dramatic. Queen Elizabeth, when she heard of it, was highly indignant, and "stormed not a little." Two years afterwards, the "bold Buccleugh" was in England, and Elizabeth was anxious to see so doughty a chieftain. He was presented accordingly, and Elizabeth, in a rough and peremptory manner, demanded of him how he had dared to undertake an enterprise so desperate and presumptuous!

"What is it," replied the undaunted Scot, "that a man dare not do?"

Elizabeth, struck with his boldness, turned to a lord in waiting, and said, "with ten thousand men such as this, our brother of Scotland might shake the firmest throne in Europe."

There is another ballad relating to the same Lord Scrope, and the execution of a noted reiver, named "Hughie the Græme," who had made woeful havoc in his time among the farmsteads of the Marches, and the cattle of "merry England." Hughie did not escape Hairibee. The actual offence for which he suffered was his stealing the Bishop of Carlisle's mare. The following is the ballad:—

HUGHIE THE GRÆME.

Gude Lord Scroope's to the hunting gane,
He has ridden our moss and muir;
And he has grippit Hughie the Græme,
For stealing o' the bishop's mare.

"Now, Good Lord Scroope, this may not be!
Here hangs a broadsword by my side;
And if that thou canst conquer me,
The matter it may soon be tryed.

"I ne'er was afraid of a traitor thief,
Although my name be Hughie the Græme;
I'll make thee repent thee of thy deeds,
If God but grant me life and time.

"Then do your worst now, good Lord Scroope,
And deal your blows as hard as you can;
It shall be tried within an hour,
Which of us two is the better man."

But as they were dealing their blows so free,
And both so bloody at the time,
Over the moss came ten yeomen so tall,
All for to take brave Hughie the Græme.

Then they ha'e gribbit Hughie the Græme,
And brought him up through Carlisle town;
The lasses and lads stood on the walls,
Crying, "Hughie the Græme, thou'se ne'er gae down!"

Then ha'e they chosen a jury of men,
The best that were in Carlisle town:
And twelve of them cried out at once,
"Hughie the Græme, thou must gae down!"

Then up bespake him gude Lord Hume,
As he sat by the judge's knee:

"Twenty white owsen, my gude Lord,
  If you'll grant Hughie the Græme to me."

"O no, O no, my gude Lord Hume!
  Forsooth, and sae it mauna be;
For were there but three Græmes of the name,
  They suld be hanged a' for me."

'Twas up and spake the gude Lady Hume,
  As she sat by the judge's knee:
"A peck of white pennies, my gude lord judge,
  If you'll grant Hughie the Græme to me."

"O no, O no, my gude Lady Hume!
  Forsooth and so it mustna be;
Were he but the one Græme of the name,
  He suld be hanged high for me."

"If I be guilty," said Hughie the Græme,
  "Of me my friends shall have small talk:"
And he has leaped fifteen feet and three,
  Tho' his hands they were tied behind his back.

He looked over his left shoulder,
  And for to see what he might see;
There was he aware of his ould father,
  Came tearing his hair most piteously.

"O hauld your tongue, my father," he says,
  "And see that ye dinna weep for me!
For they may ravish me o' my life,
  But they canna banish me fro' heaven hie.

"Fare ye weel, fair Maggie, my wife!
  The last time we came ower the muir,
'Twas thou bereft me of my life,
  And wi' the bishop thou play'd the whore.

"Here, Johnnie Armstrong, take thou my sword,
  That is made o' the metal sae fine;
And when thou comest to the English side,
  Remember the death of Hughie the Græme."

There are two or more versions of the foregoing: one in Ritson's Collection; and one communicated by Burns to Johnson's Museum. The ballad of Hobbie Noble relates to a hero of the same stamp, who suffered about the same period, at the same place, for a similar love for English oxen and sheep.

Hobbie was an Englishman; who, finding less difference in the laws of "mine and thine" on the Scotch side of the border, and more sympathy with such loose notions of property as he possessed, established himself among the Scotch, and helped them to ravage the country to Carlisle southward, whenever opportunity offered. The Scotch, however, proved false to him. The Armstrongs, amongst whom he was residing, were bribed by the English to decoy him over the border upon pretence of a raid or foray; where he was delivered up to a party from Carlisle castle, that had long been on the look-out for him. By these he was taken to Carlisle, and hanged on Hairibee in less than twenty-four hours afterwards.

HOBBIE NOBLE.

Foul fa' the breast first treason bred in!
That Liddesdale may safely say:
For in it there was baith meat and drink,
And corn unto our geldings gay.

And we were a' stout-hearted men,
As England she might often say;
But now we may turn our backs and flee,
Since brave Noble is sold away.

Now Hobbie was an Englishman,
And born in Bewcastle dale;
But his misdeeds they were so great,
They banished him to Liddesdale.

At Kershope foot the tryst was set,
Kershope of the lilye lee;
And there was traitor Sim o' the Mains,
And with him a private companie.

Then Hobbie has graithed his body fair,
Baith wi' the iron and wi' the steil;
And he has ta'en out his fringed gray,
And there brave Hobbie he rade him weel.

Then Hobbie is down the water gane,
E'en as fast as he could hie!
Tho' a' should ha'e bursten and broken their hearts,
Frae that riding tryst he wad na be.

"Weel be ye met, my feres five!
And now, what is your will wi' me?"
Then they cried a' wi' ae consent,
Thou'rt welcome here, brave Noble, to me.

"Wilt thou with us into England ride,
And thy safe warrand we will be?
If we get a horse worth a hundred pound,
Upon his back thou sune sall be."

"I dare not by day into England ride,
The land-serjeant has me at feid;
And I know not what evil may betide,
For Peter of Whitfield, his brother is dead.

"And Anton Shiel he loves not me,

For I gat twa drifts o' his sheep;
The great Earl of Whitfield loves me not,
For nae gear frae me he e'er couldkeep.

"But will ye stay till the day gae down,
Until the night come o'er the grund,
And I'll be a guide worth ony twa
That may in Liddesdale be found?

"Though the night be black as pick andtar
I'll guide ye o'er yon hill sae hie,
And bring ye a' in safety back,
If ye'll be true and follow me."

He has guided them o'er moss and muir,
O'er hill and hope, and mony a down;
Until they came to the Foulbogshiel,
And there, brave Noble, he lighted down.

But word is gane to the land serjeant,
In Askerton where that he lay—
"The deer that ye ha'e hunted sae lang,
Is seen into the Waste this day."

"Then Hobbie Noble is that deer!
I wot he carries the style fu' hie;
Aft has he driven our bluidhounds back,
And set ourselves at little lee.

"Gar warn the bows of Hartlie burn;
See they sharp their arrows on thewa';
Warn Willeva and Speir Edom,
And see the morn they meet me a'.

"Gar meet me on the Rodric-haugh,
And see it be by break o' day:
And we will on to Conscouthart-green,
For there, I think, we'll get our prey."

Then Hobbie Noble has dreimita dreim,
In the Foulbogsheil, where thathe lay;
He dreimit his horse was aneith him shot,
And he himself got hard away.

The cocks could craw, the day could daw,
And I wot sae even fell down the rain;
Had Hobbie na awakened at that time,

In the Foulbogshiel he had been ta'en or slain.

"Awake, awake, my feres five!
I trow here make a fu' ill day;
Yet the worst cloak o' this company,
I hope shall cross the Waste this day."

Now Hobbie thought the gates were clear,
But even, alas! it was na sae;
They were beset by cruel men and keen
That away brave Hobbie might na gae.

"Yet follow me, my feres five,
And see ye keip of me guid ray;
And the worst cloak o' this company,
Even yet may cross the Waste this day."

But the land-serjeant's men came Hobbie before,
The traitor Sim came Hobbie behin',
So had Noble been wight as Wallace was,
Away, alas! he might na win.

Then Hobbie had but a laddie's sword,
But he did mair than a laddie's deed;
For that sword had cleared Conscouthart-green,
Had it not broke o'er Jerswigham's head.

Then they ha'e ta'en brave HobbieNoble,
Wi's ain bowstring the band him sae;
But his gentle heart was ne'er sae sair,
As when his ain five bound him on the brae.

They ha'e ta'en him on for west Carlisle;
They asked him if he ken'd the way?
Though much he thought, yet little hesaid;
He knew the gate as weel as they.

They ha'e ta'en him up the Ricker-gate;
The wives they cast their windowswide;
And every wife to another can say;
"That's the man loosed Jock o' the Side!"

"Fy on ye, woman, why ca' ye me man?
For it's nae man that I'm used like;
Am but like a forfoughen hound,
Has been fighting in a dirty syke."

They ha'e had him up through Carlisle town,
And set him by the chimney fire;
They gave brave Noble a loaf to eat,
And that was little his desire,

They gave him a wheaten loaf to eat,
And after that a can of beer;
And they a' cried with one consent,
"Eat, brave Noble, and make gude cheir!

"Confess my lord's horse, Hobbie," they said,
"And to-morrow in Carlisle thou's na die."
"How can I confess them," Hobbie says,
"When I never saw them with my e'e?"

The Hobbie has sworn a fu' great aith,
By the day that he was gotten and born,
He never had onything o' my lord's,
That either eat him grass or corn.

"Now fare thee weel, sweet Mangerton!
For I think again I'll ne'er thee see:
I wad ha'e betrayed nae lad nor alive,
For a' the gowd o' Christentie.

"And fare thee weel, sweet Liddesdale!
Baith the hie land and the law;
Keep ye weel frae the traitor Mains!
For gowd and gear he'll sell ye a'.

"Yet wad I rather be ca'd Hobbie Noble,
In Carlisle where he suffers for his fau't,
Than I'd be ca'd the traitor Mains,
That eats and drinks o' the meal and maut."

Referring the reader to Percy's *Reliques* for "Adam Bell, Clym of the Clough, and William of Cloudesley," a long and interesting ballad of this period, or somewhat earlier, we conclude this portion of the poetical antiquities of Carlisle by a very beautiful and touching ballad, "the lament of the border widow." It is founded upon the story of Cockburn of Henderland, a noted disturber of the English districts; who did not, however, suffer at Carlisle, though he had ravaged its neighbourhood; nor at the hands of the English, whose laws he had violated. James the Fifth, scandalized at the excesses of these border reivers, made an excursion into their country in 1529, and executed summary justice upon several of the most turbulent and lawless of them, including the famous Johnnie Armstrong, Adam Scot of Tushielaw, and

Cockburn of Henderland.

The latter was hanged, by the King's order, over the gate of his own keep, or tower, while his lady fled to the banks of a mountain-stream, called the Henderland burn, and sat down at the foot of a foaming cataract, to drown, amid the sound of the roaring waters, the noise of the drums that announced the close of her husband's existence. The place where she sat is still shown to the stranger. The author of the ballad is unknown. It was taken down from recitation in the Ettrick forest, and is as affecting a ballad as any in the language, abounding with touches of genuine pathos, and most lovely simplicity of sorrow. Exquisite is the whole composition; and many of the passages are worthy of the greatest of poets.

My love, he built me a bonny bower,
And clad it a' wi' lilye flower,
A brawer bower ye ne'er did see,
Than my true love he built for me.

There came a man by middle day,
He spied his sport and went away,
And brought the King that very night,
Who brake my bower and slew my knight.

He slew my knight, to me sae dear,
He slew my knight and poined his gear;
My servants all for life did flee,
And left me in extremitie.

I sewed his sheet, making my moan;
I watched the corpse myself alone;
I watched the body night and day,
No living creature came that way.

I took his body on my back,
And whiles I gaed, and whiles I sat,
I digged a grave and laid him in,
And happed him with the sod sae green.

But think na ye my heart was sair,
When I laid the mould on his yellow hair!
O think na ye my heart was wae
When I turned about away to gae!

Nae living man I'll love again,
Since that my lovely knight is slain;
Wi' ae lock of his yellow hair

I'll bind my heart for evermair.

The devoted wife was buried with her husband. In a deserted burial place, which once surrounded the keep of Henderland, the monument was lately, and perhaps is still, to be seen. It is a large stone, broken into three parts, but some armorial bearings are traceable, and the following inscription—legible though much defaced, "HERE LYES PERYS OF COKBURNE AND HIS WYFE, MARJORY."

During the civil wars with the "Roses," Carlisle suffered severely; sometimes from the one party and sometimes from the other—a calamity which it shared, however, with all the other principal towns of the kingdom. In the formidable rising against Henry the Eighth, led originally by Sir Robert Aske, and known as the Pilgrimage of Grace, the city was besieged by 8000 men. They were under the command of Nicholas Musgrave, Thomas Gilley, and others, who appeared as leaders of the movement, after it had been abandoned by Aske and its other originators. The citizens, knowing that the Duke of Norfolk was marching to their relief, sallied out upon their besiegers, and put them to flight. Seventy of the leaders were captured by the Duke; but Musgrave, the prime mover, escaped. The others were hanged and beheaded, and their heads placed upon the gates of the city. This happened in the year 1537.

Little more than a century afterwards, Carlisle suffered a severer siege by the Scotch and Parliamentary forces, under General Lesley. It was defended for the Royalists by Sir Thomas Glenham; and surrendered on the 28th of June, 1645, after having held out for more than six months. During the siege, the distress of the garrison and the inhabitants was so severe, that the flesh of horses, dogs, rats, and other vermin was eaten. Bread was exhausted and hemp-seed substituted; which in its turn became so dear as to be unpurchasable by all except the most wealthy. A coinage of silver pieces, of three shillings value, was instituted in the castle during the siege, from the plate of the inhabitants, which was sent in for the purpose. The diary of Isaac Tullie, a resident in the city during the siege, preserved among the Harleian MSS. in the British Museum, states that "the citizens were so shrunk from starvation, that they could not choose but laugh at one another, to see their clothes hang upon them as upon men on gibbets, for one might put one's head and fists between the doublets and shirts of many of them."

THE DRUIDS' SACRIFICE.

A LEGEND OF KESWICK.

Mark yon altar
... See this wide circus
Skirted with unhewn stone; they awe my soul,
As if the very Genius of the place
Himself appeared, and with terrific tread
Stalked through his drear domain....
Know that thou stand'st on consecrated ground—
The mighty pile of magic-planted rocks,
Thus ranged in mystic order, marks the place
Where but at times of holiest festival
The Druid led his train.

MASON.

The old road between Keswick and Penrith passes over a rough hill, called Castle Rigg, which the new road now avoids. In a field adjoining this road, on the right hand side going to Penrith, just on the crown of the hill, and at the distance of a mile and a-half east by north from Keswick, are the remains of a Druidical Temple, popularly named the Druids' Stones.

These interesting memorials of the primeval age of Britain consist of forty-eight rude, unhewn blocks of granite, thirty-eight of which are disposed in an oval figure, of which the diameter is thirty-four yards from north to south, and nearly thirty from east to west: the remaining ten stones form an oblong square on the eastern side of the oval area. The latter enclosure, which is seven yards by three, is supposed to have been the sacred place, exclusively appropriated to the Druidical order, where the priests assembled to perform their mystical rites, and to determine on matters of government and judicature. The largest of the stones is upwards of seven feet in height, and may weigh about eight tons, but the greater number measure only three or four feet in height; they mostly stand in an erect position.

The situation of this ancient place for superstitious worship has been skilfully chosen, when considered with reference to the idolatrous superstitions of the Druids; the objects of which were to subdue the mind with appalling images, and to extort obedience through the agency of terror. It is seated in the neighbourhood of Skiddaw, Blencathara, and Helvellyn, and some of the highest mountains of Cumberland, whose clouded summits impended over the sacrificial altar, casting obscure shadows through its precincts. Hither the trembling worshippers repaired, to hear and to acknowledge the teachings and denunciations of their potent masters. In the eyes of the barbarian Britons, alike ignorant, credulous, and superstitious, the place would appear to be the very sanctuary of Omnipotence, and the Druid ministers themselves an impersonation of their gods. Wind and cloud, storm and tempest, wrought powerfully in the abstruse mysteries and terrific incantations constituting the Druidical worship; and the mind was prostrated, with terrific awe, at the shrine where natural sublimity combined with human cunning to thrill its scarcely awakened faculties. Here, at midnight, every Druid, summoned by the terrible horn, never sounded but upon high occasions, and descending from his mountain or secret cave, might assemble, without intrusion from one sacrilegious footstep, and celebrate a festival.

> "By rites of such strange potency,
> As, done in open day, would dim the sun,
> Though 'throned in noontide brightness."

The tourist will tread this once hallowed circle, where the Druids offered their adorations to Deity, and sat in judgment on their fellow-men, with a mixture of awe and veneration, so well expressed by the poet:—

> "Skirted with unhewn stone, it awes my soul
> As if the very Genius of the place
> Himself appeared, and with terrific tread
> Stalked through this drear domain."

In spite of the ravages of time, assisted by the destructive hand of man, many Druidical monuments still remain amongst the seclusions of the lakes and mountains of Cumberland and Westmoreland, and many are the strange tales connected with them. For the interest of our readers, we select the following:
—

In times long gone by, when these mountains reared their naked heads to the clouds—when their sides were clothed with oak, and their feet were wet with morasses—when the wild cow and the wolf contested the mastership of the unclaimed property—when human feet had never trod these hills or vales—a mighty warrior left his companions in the south and journeyed hitherward. His followers, as they traversed the forests towards the north, met with a beautiful river, at the foot of a gentle hill, well clothed with wood. The warrior said to his companions, let us here construct our tents. Here is wood for shelter and fire; and this river and these mountains will supply us with food.

Then they fixed poles in the ground, and fastened them together with wicker-work of branches, and covered them with the green sod from the ground. And the warrior said, the old oak trees around our dwellings will shelter us from the storm in winter, and shade us from the sun in summer. Thus they continued to pass the time in hunting the wild deer among the hills, and in fishing in the adjoining river; and as they were not disturbed by wars, they rapidly increased in strength and numbers.

Their ancient priests or Druids retired farther north, because their solemn rites required the greatest privacy; and the mistletoe, their sacred emblem, abounded more among the northern forests. Besides, stones to construct their temples of were more easily procured among these hills; and being far from the haunts of men, they could indulge in the gloomy contemplation of the vindictive character of the Deity—for they knew him only as a Being capable of revenging every insult offered to His name.

When their town was become very populous, there lived in it a youth of superior strength and agility, who was remarked for being particularly expert with the bow, and so swift that few could outstrip him in the race. At feats of strength or skill, he was ever foremost: and, in attacking the wolf, or the wild cow, few possessed so daring a soul. It is an old maxim, with few exceptions, that love is the companion of bravery—and Mudor loved the gentle Ella. They had retired, at an early age, to a grove farther up the river, where stood the image of their God Mogan, which had been purchased of some Phenician merchants, along with some iron hatchets, in exchange for the skins of beasts, slain in the chase. Before this rude representation of the Deity they mutually pledged their vows; and to render those pledges more binding, they each stained a blue sun on their breasts, as a memorial that their faith should be as durable as the light of that luminary. No one felt so proud on hearing the praise of Mudor as Ella did—no one hailed his return from the chase, loaded with spoils, with the warmth of Ella—nor did any one so much admire the elegance of the blue symbols of his prowess and his faith, which were painted on his skin, as did the faithful Ella. Reared in two adjoining cabins, their infant sports had been together. For her he had plunged into the morass to procure the richest and sweetest water-lilies—he had climbed the loftiest oak to gain the cushat eggs—and the scarf of squirrel skins which screened her from the cold, was the produce of his most early adventures in the chase. Thus circumstanced, their hearts were knit together by those ties which bind the savage as well as the civilized; for the heart of the naked Indian who treads the burning sands of the desert is as warm to the tender impressions of love as the prince who stretches his limbs on a silken couch, or reposes on a bed of down.

These faithful lovers dreamt of no unkindly fate interfering, when a fever broke out in the town, and swept away a number of its inhabitants. Application was made to the priest of Mogan to avert the awful visitation by prayer; but he returned for answer, that the wickedness of the people had offended the Great Invisible, and the fever was sent as a just punishment. The Druids, therefore, who resided in the neighbourhood, made a pilgrimage to one of their largest temples, situated among the mountains, in the midst of a vast forest. The Arch-Druid, having gathered the mistletoe, just as the rising sun licked the dew from its berries, and performed a number of other rites, to obtain answer from the Great Spirit, informed them that Heaven would not be appeased unless a young virgin was immolated as a sacrifice for the sins of the inhabitants. When this intelligence was announced, the utmost dismay seized on every heart. Parents trembled for their daughters, and the daughters trembled for themselves; for no one knew on whom the lot would fall.

The Druids of the neighbouring groves assembled together, and cast lots, according to their established usage. The lot fell on Ella! Sad was the heart of Mudor when he heard this; and vainly did he entreat that some other victim might be selected in her stead. It was the irrevocable decree of heaven, and the priests had not the power to alter it. No one felt the sentence less severely than Ella did. She resigned herself to the will of the Deity; and would not render unavailable the sacrifice by any vain and foolish complaints. Still the affection she felt for Mudor would steal across her mind, and a momentary wish that she might have lived to fulfil her vows would interrupt her devotional complacency.

The morning arrived when Ella was to be conveyed far into the deserts, among the northern mountains, to the gloomy dell, where Heaven would alone be appeased. Mudor, at a humble distance, followed the procession of the Druids, and separating himself from the crowd which usually assembled to witness those awful rites of the Druid priests, appeared like one who had no conception of what was passing before him. They at length arrived at the place of sacrifice, which was a gloomy dell, in the midst of a forest, near the banks of a river, surrounded by magnificent scenery. This dell was a curious cavity in the rock, of considerable extent, and rendered almost dark by the overhanging branches of the ancient oaks which grew above it. A small circular area, surrounded with large upright stones, was the place of sacrifice. The priests assembled to perform their horrid rites; while the gaping crowd hung in the fissures of the rock on each side, or sat on the branches of the trees, waiting the celebration of the awful ceremony. The bards, with their heads crowned with oak, advanced to the north side of the circle; and after paying obedience to the sun, they chanted the following hymn:—

"Being great, who reign'st alone,

Veiled in clouds, unseen, unknown,
Centre of the vast profound,
Clouds of darkness close thee round.

"Thy nod makes storms and tempests rise,
Thy breath makes thunder shake the skies,
Thy frown turns noon-day into night,
And makes the sun withdraw his light.

"Beneath thy anger we expire,
The victims of thy vengeful ire;
Destruction rules at thy command,
And ruin blackens all the land."

A small cabin of basket-work was erected near the western side of the circle, in the lowest part of the dell, with a door opening towards the Druidical circle. In this the youthful Ella was to be immolated. She was brought into the circle; a garland of oak leaves was bound round her neck, a chaplet of wild flowers placed on her head, and a piece of mistletoe in her hand. Thus adorned she was led to the centre of the circle, and supported there by two aged priests, while the bards chanted the following invocation to the sun:—

FIRST BARD.

"See, thy destined victim see,
Bright, and chaste, and pure as thee,
Let this sinless virgin please thee,
Sinful man could ne'er appease thee."

SECOND BARD.

"Round her brows the wild flowers see,
Emblems of thy purity—
Touch'd by mortal's fingers never;—
Round her breast the oak survey,
Which like thee can ne'er decay—
Innocence endures for ever."

THIRD BARD.

"Spirit! who no birth has known,
Springing from thyself alone,
We thy living emblem show
In the mystic mistletoe:—
Springs and grows without a root—
Yields without flower its fruit—
Seeks from earth no mother's care—
Lives and blooms the child of air."

FOURTH BARD.

"Thou dost thy mystic circle trace
  Along the vaulted blue profound,
And, emblematic of thy race,
  We tread our mystic circle round."

ALL THE BARDS.

"Shine upon us, mighty God—
  Raise this drooping world of ours—
Send from thy divine abode,
  Cheering sun and fruitful showers."

The lovely Ella was then enclosed in the wicker cabin: a quantity of dry withered leaves, and small dry branches, were laid all round the cabin ready to set fire to. Every one of the crowd was obliged to furnish at least one stick towards producing a fire to consume the victim. But Mudor stood at a distance, determined rather to incur the vengeance of the Invisible Spirit than add one particle to the destruction of his adorable Ella. The Arch-Druid took two pieces of wood, and exposing them to the sun, rubbed them together, while all the bards chanted the following verse:—

"Sun descend in a ray of light,
Wrapp'd in thy power and clad in thy might;
Come in a red and a fiery stream,
Come in a bright and glowing beam;
Come in thy flaming chariot down,
Burn the wood in a flame of thy own."

The friction of the two pieces of wood had the desired effect—they took fire. The sticks and leaves round the cabin which contained the ill-fated Ella were instantly in a blaze. As the flames arose the bards chanted, with loud voices, the following verses:—

"Mighty Sovereign of the skies,
Accept this virgin sacrifice,
Let her spotless soul atone
For wicked actions not her own.
As to death her spirit stoops,
As she faints and as she droops,
Lay aside thy fiery crown
And spare, O spare, her native town!
She was good, and she was kind,
And she possess'd a heavenly mind;
Wicked man could ne'er atone

For his sins and crimes alone,
A purer victim must be found
To wash the stain away."

The bards stopped short, and raised their hands with astonishment—the crowd shrieked out with fear—and all the rites were suspended; for at that moment a flood of water burst out from the fissures of the rock on every side, and came rolling down the dell like a river. The wicket hurdle in which Ella was confined was instantly surrounded by the flood—the fire was quenched, and she came out unhurt. It is said that a voice was heard by the Arch-Druid of solemn import, intimating that human victims were not acceptable to the Deity—that a greater sacrifice was about to be offered—and that the reign of Druidism was at an end. The Arch-Druid, turning his face towards the sun for a moment, and then to the other priests, remarked that some mighty change was surely about to take place among them; for this was a miracle they could have no conception of.

The assembly dispersed in consternation; and the devoted Ella was happily restored to the arms of the overjoyed Mudor, with whom she lived to a good old age; and the rock has occasionally poured forth its stream ever since.

THE HEIGHTS OF HELVELLYN;

OR, THE UNFORTUNATE TOURIST.

IN making an ascent of Helvellyn, some tourists are bold enough to traverse the giddy and dangerous heights of Striding Edge: "but this road," says the Bard of the Lakes, "ought not to be taken by any one with weak nerves, as the top in many places scarcely affords room to plant the foot, and is beset with awful precipices on either side." The path on one part of the pass is certainly not more than two yards broad, and a tremendous precipice descending on each side makes it truly appalling and perilous.

Mr. Baines, who, with a companion, ascended Helvellyn by this pass some years ago, thus describes it:—"The ridge we were upon—Striding Edge—was the shorter but more rugged path; and, in spite of the warnings of our boatman, we chose it, being incited by curiosity, and perhaps quite as much by the motive which actuates most men in fighting duels—a fear lest our courage should be called in question if we declined the danger. We therefore addressed ourselves to the passage of Striding Edge; but if we had seen the most dangerous part before we came to it, we should have been content to take the safer though more cowardly branch of the alternative offered to us. As we ascended, the hill became more steep and rugged, till at length the ridge presented nothing but rocks, the narrow edges of which lay upwards in the direction of the sky. Their sides became steeper and steeper, and it was with difficulty that we crept along paths not wider than a goat-track, to avoid clambering among the crags which formed the very ridge of the hill. At length it became impossible to find footing on the side, and we betook ourselves of necessity to the ridge itself. We now came in view of the most formidable part of Striding Edge, and found that it rather deserved to be compared to a narrow wall, several hundred feet in height, connecting the hill which we had been ascending with the head of the mountain, than to the steep roof of a house. It appeared to us to be absolutely precipitous on each side, and the top of the rocky wall was not more than from one to two yards wide, whilst in some places we could not see, before we came to it, as much ground as would serve to plant a foot upon—the rocks presenting their sharp and rugged edges upwards, like slates or tiles standing on end. If we had had a guide, all this would have been much less terrific, because he would have led the way, and shown us where to place every footstep. The possibility that we might, after all, have taken a wrong direction, or that in some part of the pass we should find ourselves in a situation where we could neither advance nor retreat, gave us considerable alarm. Neither of us, however, expressed our fears at the time; and I felt myself bound to keep up both my own spirits and George's, as the blame would have been chiefly mine if any accident had happened. I therefore talked loudly and confidently as we scrambled along, keeping all my eyes about me, and giving him such instructions as his want of experience in climbing rendered necessary. He said little or nothing, and never ventured to cast a look either at the tarn which lay several hundred feet below us on one side, or to the equally awful depth on the other; but, fixing his eyes on the ridge itself as if he were fascinated, he crept on after me as cautiously and yet as fast as he could. In this way we crossed the long and dangerous pass of Striding Edge, till we came to the last ascent of the mountain."

A melancholy interest attaches to this spot, from the fate of a young man who perished in its locality some years ago. It was here that Charles Gough, of Manchester, a frequent visitor to the Lakes, met with an accident which caused his death. This unfortunate "young lover of nature," confiding in his knowledge of the country, attempted to cross Helvellyn from Patterdale to Wythburn by the pass of Striding Edge just described. He set out late one afternoon early in the spring of 1805, without any guide, and attended by no companion but his faithful dog. Darkness, it is supposed, came on before his expectation, and a fall of snow having partially concealed the path, rendered it still more dangerous. He wandered from the track, and his body was found in one of those deep recesses where human foot rarely treads. It could never be ascertained whether he was killed by falling from the rocks, or he perished from hunger. Let us hope that death came with friendly care to shorten sufferings that might have been yet more awful.

Three months elapsed before his remains were discovered; when the faithful dog, which was his constant attendant during frequent solitary rambles amidst the wilds of Cumberland and Westmorland, was discovered still watching over the lifeless remains of his master. This striking and affecting instance of canine faithfulness has been commemorated by Wordsworth in his beautiful poem entitled *Fidelity*.

A barking sound the shepherd hears,
   A cry as of a dog or fox;
He halts, and searches with his eyes
   Among the scattered rocks:
And now at distance can discern
A stirring in a brake of fern;
And instantly a dog is seen,
Glancing through that covert green.

The dog is not of mountain breed;

Its motions too are wild and shy;
With something, as the shepherd thinks,
Unusual in its cry.
Nor is there any one in sight
All round, in hollow, or on height:
Nor shout, nor whistle, strikes the ear;
What is the creature doing here?

It was a cove, a huge recess,
That keeps till June December's snow;
A lofty precipice in front,
A silent tarn below!
Far in the bosom of Helvellyn,
Remote from public road or dwelling,
Pathway, or cultivated land,
From trace of human foot or hand.

There, sometimes doth the leaping fish
Send through the tarn a lonely cheer;
The crag repeats the raven's croak,
In symphony austere;
Thither the rainbow comes—the cloud—
And mists that spread the flying shroud;
And sunbeams, and the sounding blast
That, if it could, would hurry past;
But that enormous barrier binds it fast.

Not free from boding thoughts awhile
The shepherd stood: then makes his way
Towards the dog, o'er rocks and stones,
As quickly as he may;
Nor far had gone before he found
A human figure on the ground;
The appall'd discoverer, with a sigh
Looks round to learn the history.

From those abrupt and perilous rocks
The man had fall'n, that place of fear!
At length upon the shepherd's mind
It breaks, and all is clear:
He instantly recall'd the name,
And who he was, and whence he came;
Remember'd too the very day,
On which the traveller pass'd this way.

But hear a wonder, for whose sake
   This lamentable tale I tell!
A lasting monument of words
   This wonder merits well.
The dog, which still was hovering nigh,
Repeating the same timid cry,
This dog had been, through three months' space,
A dweller in that savage place.

Yes, proof was plain, that since that day,
   When this ill-fated traveller died,
The dog had watched about the spot,
   Or by his master's side:
How nourish'd here through such long time,
He knows, who gave that love sublime;
And gave that strength of feeling, great,
Above all human estimate.

The melancholy circumstances connected with the death of Charles Gough have also been beautifully depicted by the powerful pen of Sir Walter Scott, who has paid a pleasing tribute to the "pilgrim of nature" in some highly pathetic stanzas, which, by the by, are rendered additionally interesting from the following anecdote connected with them:—"Our two charming poets, Walter Scott and Campbell, walking together" (says Ryan, in his *Poetry and the Poets*), "and speaking of this incident, each agreed, in the spirit of amicable rivalship, to make it the subject of a poem. Scott, on his way home, composed the following exquisite lines, which he sent the next day to Campbell, who returned them with this reply:—'I confess myself vanquished: if I were to live a thousand years, I could never write anything equal to this, on the same subject;' and he never attempted it."

I climbed the dark brow of the mighty Helvellyn,
   Lakes and mountains beneath me gleamed misty and wide;
All was still—save by fits, when the eagle was yelling,
   And, starting around me, the echoes replied.
On the right, Striding Edge round the Red Tarn was bending,
And Catchedecam its left verge was defending,
One huge nameless rock in front was impending,
   When I marked the sad spot where the wanderer died.

Dark green was that spot, 'mid the brown mountain heather,
   Where the pilgrim of nature lay stretched in decay,
Like the corpse of an outcast, abandoned to weather,
   Till the mountain winds wasted the tenantless clay:

Not yet quite deserted, though lonely extended,
For faithful in death, his mute favourite attended,
The much-loved remains of his master defended,
And chased the hill-fox and the raven away.

How long didst thou think that his silence was slumber—
When the wind waved his garments how oft didst thou start
—
How many long days and long nights didst thou number,
Ere he faded before thee, the friend of thy heart?—
And ah! was it meet that no requiem read o'er him;
No mother to weep, and no friend to deplore him;
And thou, little guardian, alone stretched before him,
Unhonoured the pilgrim from life should depart?

When a prince to the fate of a peasant has yielded,
The tapestry waves dark round the dim-lighted hall;
With escutcheons of silver the coffin is shielded,
And the pages stand mute by the canopied pall;
Through the courts, at deep midnight, the torches are
gleaming,
In the proudly arched chapel the banners are beaming,
Far adown the long aisle sacred music is streaming,
Lamenting a chief of the people should fall.

But meeter for thee, gentle lover of nature,
To lay down thy head like the meek mountain lamb,
When, wildered, he drops from some rock high in stature,
And draws his last breath by the side of his dam:
And more stately thy couch by this desert lake lying,
Thy obsequies sung by the gray plover flying,
With but one faithful friend to witness thy dying,
In the arms of Helvellyn and Catchedecam.

Charles Gough is said to have been a young gentleman of talent, and of an amiable disposition. His remains peacefully repose in the chapel-yard at Patterdale.

THE REGATTA;

OR, THE LOVERS OF DERWENTWATER.

AN annual regatta takes place on Derwentwater, when the several sports of racing, rowing, and wrestling, are maintained with great spirit.

The following is an excellent description of one of these occasions in former times:—"At eight o'clock in the morning a vast concourse of ladies and gentlemen appeared on the side of Derwent Lake, where a number of marquees, extending about 400 yards, were erected for their accommodation. At twelve, such of the company as were invited by Mr. Pocklington passed over in boats to the island which bears his name; and, on their landing, were saluted by a discharge of his artillery, consisting of five four pounders and one nine pounder. This might properly be called the opening of the regatta; for as soon as the echo of this discharge had ceased, a signal gun was fired, and five boats, which lay upon their oars (on that part of the lake which runs nearest the town of Keswick), instantly pushed off the shore and began the race. A view from any of the attendant boats, of which there were several, presented a scene which beggars all description. The sides of the hoary mountains were clad with spectators, and the glassy surface of the lake was variegated with numbers of pleasure barges, which, trimmed out in all the gayest colours, and glittering in the rays of the meridian sun, gave a new appearance to the celebrated beauties of this matchless vale. The contending boats passed Pocklington's Island, and rounding St. Herbert's Isle and Rampsholme, edged down by the outside of Lord's Island, describing, in the race, almost a perfect circle, and, during the greatest part of it, in full view of the company.

"About three o'clock preparations were made for a sham attack on Pocklington's Island. The fleet, consisting of several barges, armed with small cannon and muskets, retired out of view, behind Friar Crag, to prepare for action; previous to which a flag of truce was sent to the governor, with a summons to surrender on honourable terms. A defiance was returned; soon after which the fleet was seen advancing with great spirit before the batteries, and instantly forming a curved line, a terrible cannonading began on both sides, accompanied with a dreadful discharge of musketry. This continued for some time, and being echoed from hill to hill in an amazing variety of sounds, filled the ear with whatever could produce astonishment and awe. All nature seemed to be in an uproar; which impressed, on the awakened imagination, the most lively ideas of "the war of elements" and "crush of worlds." After a severe conflict, the enemies were driven from the attack in great disorder. A *feu-de-joie* was then fired in the port, and oft repeated by the responsive echoes. The fleet, after a little delay, formed again; and practising a variety of beautiful manœuvres, renewed the attack. Uproar again sprung up, and the deep-toned echoes of the mountains again joined in solemn chorus; which was heard at the distance of ten leagues to leeward, through the easterly opening of that vast amphitheatre, as far as Appleby.

"The garrison at last capitulated; and the entertainment of the water being finished, towards the evening the company rowed to Keswick, to which place, from the water's edge, a range of lamps was fixed, very happily disposed, and a number of fire-works played off. An assembly room, which was built for the purpose, next received the ladies and gentlemen, and a dance concluded this annual festivity.

"Whilst we sat to regale, the barge put off from shore, to a station where the finest echoes were to be obtained from the surrounding mountains. The vessel was provided with six brass cannon, mounted on swivels; on discharging one of these pieces the report was echoed from the opposite rocks, where, by reverberation, it seemed to roll from cliff to cliff, and return through every cave and valley, till the decreasing tumult died away upon the ear.

"The instant it ceased the sound of every distant waterfall was heard; but for an instant only; for the momentary stillness was interrupted by the returning echo on the hills behind; where the report was repeated like a peal of thunder bursting over our heads, continuing for several seconds, flying from haunt to haunt, till once more the sound gradually declined. Again the voice of waterfalls possessed the interval, till to the right the more distant thunders arose upon some other mountains, and seemed to take its way up every winding dale and creek; sometimes behind, on this side, or on that, in wondrous speed running its dreadful course; when the echo reached the mountains within the line and channel of the breeze, it was heard at once on the right and left at the extremities of the lake. In this manner was the report of every discharge re-echoed seven times distinctly."

The following descriptive poem appeared on the occasion of a regatta at Keswick:—

"Scarcely had day's bright god begun his course,
And chas'd the misty vapours from the lake,
When, ardent all for pleasure, forth there sprung
A bright assemblage of firm, active youths,
And virgins blushing like the op'ning bud.
Nay, some there were who sought the sportive scene
Whom frozen age had bow'd with iron hand;
Drawn by the force of curiosity,
Or by the workings of parental care,
To watch and guard their blooming daughter's steps.
The neigh'bouring rustics, too, with massy limbs,
Inur'd to toil, inur'd to fun and rain;
Each led his fav'rite damsel to the sight,

And talk'd of love, or laugh'd with hearty roar.

"And now the vessels all in orderrange,
To try the fortune of the wat'ry race.
The rowers sit; their eyes with ardour glow,
Attentive watching the appointed sign.
And now the gun, the signal for the course.
Rends with its iron voice th' o'ervaulting sky,
And distant rocks, redoubling, echo back
The horrid note. Instantly they start,
And, adverse looking, try their utmost skill.
Big swells each bulky muscle, strain'd with toil;
O'er their knit brows the drops of labour pour,
Whilst on their faces anxious fear and hope
Alternate sit depicted. Now they come
Almost within the grasp of victory:
Then, then what rapture fires the victor's mind,
When with his toil-strained arm he shakes the flag,
And shouts, applauding, echo all around.

"Now o'er the azure lake the horrid din
Of mimic war resounds; the echoing cliffs
Reverberate, in doubled thunder, back
The awful sounds: fierce peal succeeds to peal,
In savage dire confusion. Had the rocks,
Which awful frown above this limpid plain,
Been shaken from their venerable seats,
Rift by the bolts of Jove, and scattered round,
No sound more loud, more awful, could be heard!
The hero, who, inur'd to bloody war,
Has stood by Elliot, or by Rodney's side,
Whilst million-winged deaths were whistling round,
Now feels his heart beat high; strong throbs each pulse,
His kindling eyes flash fire: upright he stands,
As when on some dread, memorable day
He saw the Frenchmen strike, or Spaniards burn.
His tender spouse, the dear, the soft reward
Of all his toils, astonish'd with the din,
Clings to his side, half-pleased and half-afraid;
When softer echoes roll the distant roar,
She smiles; but when the air-affrighting guns
With iron clamours shake th' impending rocks,
She trembling presses hard her husband's hand,

And weeps to think the perils he has 'scap'd.

"But hark! 'tis silent! see, the fleet retires!
The mellow horns now pour victorious sounds,
Whilst every rock returns the softened strain.
O! now for Shakspeare, or for Milton's muse,
To paint this mingled tide of harmony!
Each cliff, each rock, each mountain, wood, and dale,
Return a varied note; it floats in air;
It mixes, meets, returns; 'tis soft, 'tis loud:
As if th' unnumber'd spirits of the rock
Held their aërial concerts 'midst the hills;
And to his golden harp each join'd his voice,
To welcome to their bower the 'Fairy Queen.'

"Thus joyous and delightful pass'd the day,
Yet not unruffled was this tide of joy:
The fair, the innocent Amelia was
The pride and flower of all the virgin throng!
Her long Damœtas loved, she too loved him,
But looks alone revealed the mutual flame,
For virgin modesty had bound their thoughts
In chains, as yet unbroken. On this day,
Whilst she in rapture viewed th' enchanting scene
(Urged by the motion of the limpid wave),
Her vessel rolling, headlong plunged her in
The blue profound! She sank, then rose again;
Then sank, to rise no more! Damœtas, near,
Beheld her fall: of life regardless then,
He leaped into the flood; with nervous arm
He cut the crystal deep, and plunging down,
Seized, and brought her up again to life.

"Restored now, she op'd her radiant eyes,
And looking gratitude ineffable,
'Is it then you, Damœtas? you whom long
My virgin heart hath own'd!' She could no more:
The rosy hue again forsook her cheek,
The light her eyes, and pallid death awhile
Seemed to return and re-demand his prey.
What then, Damœtas, were the dire alarms
That rent thy manly bosom? Love, despair,
Grief, and astonishment, exert at once

The utmost of their force to tear thy soul!
But see, the rose again resumes its seat
Upon her cheek! again her op'ning eye
Beams softened lustre! Kneeling by her side
Damœtas press'd her hand; in falt'ring words
Propos'd his am'rous suit. Her parents near,
Relieved now from the heart-corroding fear,
First poured in tender words their grateful hearts,
Then to Damœtas gave the willing hand
Of their beloved Amelia. Instant joy
Flushed lively in his cheek, and fired his heart
With all the rapt'rous bliss of mutual love.
He tried in vain to speak, for words, alas!
Could ill express tumultuous joys like his;
He stammer'd, blush'd, and thanked them in thought.

"And now the fiery charioteer of day
Drove down the western steep his blazing car,
When homeward all return to close their sports,
And usher in with dance the sable night.
The sprightly music sounds, the youths advance,
And blooming virgins from the beauteous group:
Then joined in couples, active as the light,
They tread the mazy dance; the swains the while
Join in sweet toil, and press the given hand,
And slyly talk of love; or else, askance,
Speak by their looks the feelings of the heart."

THE SHEPHERD OF GREEN-HEAD GHYLL.

A TALE OF GRASMERE VALE.

IF from the public way you turn your steps
Up the tumultuous brook of Green-head Ghyll,
You will suppose that with an upright path
Your feet must struggle; in such bold ascent
The pastoral mountains front you, face to face.
But, courage! for around that boisterous brook
The mountains have all opened out themselves,
And made a hidden valley of their own.
No habitation can be seen; but they
Who journey thither find themselves alone
With a few sheep, with rocks and stones, and kites
That overhead are sailing in the sky.
It is in truth an utter solitude;
Nor should I have made mention of this dell
But for one object which you might pass by—
Might see and notice not. Beside the brook
Appears a straggling heap of unhewn stones!
And to that place a story appertains,
Which, though it be ungarnished with events,
Is not unfit, I deem, for the fireside,
Or for the summer shade. It was the first
Of those domestic tales that spake to me
Of shepherds, dwellers in the valleys, men
Whom I already loved:—not verily
For their own sakes, but for the fields and hills
Where was their occupation and abode.
And hence this tale, while I was yet a boy
Careless of books, yet having felt the power
Of nature, by the gentle agency
Of natural objects led me on to feel
For passions that were not my own, and think
(At random and imperfectly indeed)
On man, the heart of man, and human life.
Therefore, although it be a history
Homely and rude, I will relate the same
For the delight of a few natural hearts:

And, with yet fonder feeling, for the sake
Of youthful poets, who among these hills
Will be my second self when I am gone.

Upon the forest-side in Grasmere Vale
There dwelt a shepherd, Michael was his name;
An old man, stout of heart, and strong of limb.
His bodily frame had been from youth to age
Of an unusual strength; his mind was keen,
Intense, and frugal, apt for all affairs,
And in his shepherd's calling he was prompt
And watchful more than ordinary men.
Hence had he learned the meaning of all winds,
Of blasts of every tone; and, oftentimes
When others heeded not, he heard the south
Make subterraneous music, like the noise
Of bagpipers on distant Highland hills.
The shepherd, at such warning, of his flock
Bethought him, and he to himself would say,
"The winds are now devising work for me!"
And, truly, at all times, the storm—that drives
The traveller to a shelter—summoned him
Up to the mountains: he had been alone
Amid the heart of many thousand mists,
That came to him and left him on the heights.
So lived he till his eightieth year was past.
And grossly that man errs, who should suppose
That the green valleys, and the streams and rocks
Were things indifferent to the shepherd's thoughts.
Fields, where with cheerful spirits he had breathed
The common air; the hills, which he so oft
Had climbed with vigorous steps; which had impressed
So many incidents upon his mind
Of hardship, skill, or courage, joy or fear;
Which like a book preserved the memory
Of the dumb animals whom he had saved,
Had fed or sheltered, linking to such acts,
So grateful in themselves, the certainty
Of honourable gain; these fields, these hills,
Which were his living being, even more
Than his own blood—what could they less? had laid
Strong hold on his affections, were to him

A pleasurable feeling of blind love,
The pleasure which there is in life itself.

His days had not been passed in singleness.
His helpmate was a comely matron, old—
Though younger than himself full twenty years.
She was a woman of a stirring life,
Whose heart was in her house: two wheels she had
Of antique form, this large for spinning wool,
That small for flax; and if one wheel had rest,
It was because the other was at work.
The pair had but one inmate in their house,
An only child, who had been born to them
When Michael, telling o'er his years, began
To deem that he was old—in shepherd's phrase,
With one foot in the grave. This only son,
With two brave sheep-dogs tried in many a storm,
The one of an inestimable worth,
Made all their household. I may truly say,
That they were as a proverb in the vale
For endless industry. When day was gone,
And from their occupations out of doors
The son and father were come home, even then,
Their labour did not cease; unless when all
Turned to their cleanly supper-board, and there,
Each with a mess of pottage and skimmed milk,
Sat round their basket piled with oaten cakes,
And their plain home-made cheese. Yet when their meal
Was ended, Luke (for so the son was named)
And his old father both betook themselves
To such convenient work as might employ
Their hands by the fireside; perhaps to card wool
For the housewife's spindle, or repair
Some injury done to sickle, flail, or scythe,
Or other implement of house or field.

Down from the ceiling, by the chimney's edge
That in our ancient uncouth country style
Did with a huge projection overbrow
Large space beneath, as duly as the light
Of day grew dim the housewife hung a lamp;
An aged utensil, which had performed
Service beyond all others of its kind.

Early at evening did it burn and late,
Surviving comrade of uncounted hours,
Which going by from year to year had found
And left the couple neither gay perhaps
Nor cheerful, yet with objects and with hopes,
Living a life of eager industry.
And now when Luke had reached his eighteenth year,
There by the light of this old lamp they sat,
Father and son, while late into the night
The housewife plied her own peculiar work.
Making the cottage through the silent hours
Murmur as with the sound of summer flies.
This light was famous in its neighbourhood,
And was a public symbol of the life
The thrifty pair had lived. For, as it chanced,
Their cottage on a plot of rising ground
Stood single, with large prospect, north and south,
High into Easedale, up to Dunmail-Raise,
And westward to the village near the lake;
And from this constant light, so regular
And so far seen, the house itself, by all
Who dwelt within the limits of the vale,
Both old and young, was named The Evening Star.

Thus living on through such a length of years,
The shepherd, if he loved himself, must needs
Have loved his helpmate; but to Michael's heart
This son of his old age was yet more dear—
Less from instinctive tenderness, the same
Blind spirit, which is in the blood of all—
Than that a child, more than all other gifts,
Brings hope with it, and forward-looking thoughts,
And stirrings of inquietude, when they
By tendency of nature needs must fail.
Exceeding was the love he bare to him,
His heart, and his heart's joy! For oftentimes
Old Michael, while he was a babe in arms,
Had done him female service, not alone
For pastime and delight, as is the use
Of fathers, but with patient mind enforced
To acts of tenderness; and he had rocked
His cradle with a woman's gentle hand.

And, in a latter time, ere yet the boy
Had put on boy's attire, did Michael love,
Albeit of a stern unbending mind,
To have the young one in his sight, when he
Had work by his own door, or when he sat
With sheep before him on his shepherd's stool,
Beneath that large old oak, which near their door
Stood—and, from its enormous breadth of shade,
Chosen for the shearer's covert from the sun,
Thence in our rustic dialect was called
The Clipping Tree,[5] a name which yet it bears.
There while they two were sitting in the shade,
With others round them, earnest all and blythe,
Would Michael exercise his heart with looks
Of fond correction and reproof bestowed
Upon the child, if he disturbed the sheep
By catching at their legs, or with his shouts
Scared them, while they lay still beneath the shears.

And when by heaven's good grace the boy grew up
A healthy lad, and carried in his cheek
Two steady roses that were five years old,
Then Michael from a winter coppice cut
With his own hands a sapling, which he hooped
With iron, making it throughout in all
Due requisites a perfect shepherd's staff,
And gave it to the boy; wherewith equipp'd
He as a watchman oftentimes was placed
At gate or gap, to stem or turn the flock;
And, to his office prematurely called,
There stood the urchin, as you will divine,
Something between a hinderance and a help;
And for this cause not always, I believe,
Receiving from his father hire of praise;
Though nought was left undone which staff, or voice,
Or looks, or threatening gestures could perform.

But soon as Luke, full ten years old, could stand
Against the mountain blasts; and to the heights,
Not fearing toil, nor length of weary ways,
He with his father daily went, and they
Were as companions, why should I relate
That objects which the shepherd loved before

Were dearer now? that from the boy there came
Feelings and emanations—things which were
Light to the sun and music to the wind;
And that the old man's heart seemed born again.

Thus in his father's sight the boy grew up:
And now when he had reached his eighteenth year,
He was his comfort and his daily hope.

While in this sort the simple household lived
From day to day, to Michael's ear there came
Distressful tidings. Long before the time
Of which I speak, the shepherd had been bound
In surety for his brother's son, a man
Of an industrious life, and ample means;
But unforeseen misfortunes suddenly
Had prest upon him, and old Michael now
Was summoned to discharge the forfeiture;
A grievous penalty, but little less
Than half his substance. This unlooked-for claim,
At the first hearing, for a moment took
More hope out of his life than he supposed
That any old man ever could have lost.
As soon as he had gathered so much strength
That he could look his trouble in the face,
It seemed that his whole refuge was to sell
A portion of his patrimonial fields.
Such was his first resolve; he thought again,
And his heart failed him. "Isabel," said he,
Two evenings after he had heard the news,
"I have been toiling more than seventy years,
And in the open sunshine of God's love
Have we all lived; yet if these fields of ours
Should pass into a stranger's hand, I think
That I could not lie quiet in my grave.
Our lot is a hard lot; the sun himself
Has scarcely been more diligent than I;
And I have lived to be a fool at last
To my own family. An evil man
That was, and made an evil choice, if he
Were false to us; and if he were not false,
There are ten thousand to whom loss like this
Had been no sorrow. I forgive him; but

'Twere better to be dumb than to talk thus.
When I began, my purpose was to speak
Of remedies and of a cheerful hope.
Our Luke shall leave us, Isabel; the land
Shall not go from us, and it shall be free;
He shall possess it, free as is the wind
That passes over it. We have, thou know'st,
Another kinsman, he will be our friend
In this distress. He is a prosperous man,
Thriving in trade, and Luke to him shall go,
And with his kinsman's help and his own thrift,
He quickly will repair this loss, and then
May come again to us. If here he stay,
What can be done? Where every one is poor,
What can be gained?" At this the old man paused,
And Isabel sat silent, for her mind
Was busy looking back into past times.
There's Richard Bateman, thought she to herself,
He was a parish-boy; at the church door
They made a gathering for him—shillings, pence,
And halfpennies, wherewith the neighbours bought
A basket, which they filled with pedlar's wares;
And, with this basket on his arm, the lad
Went up to London, found a master there,
Who out of many, chose the trusty boy
To go and overlook his merchandize
Beyond the seas; where he grew wondrous rich,
And left estates and monies to the poor,
And at his birth-place built a chapel, floored
With marble which he sent from foreign lands.
These thoughts and many others of like sort,
Passed quickly through the mind of Isabel,
And her face brightened. The old man was glad,
And thus resumed:—"Well, Isabel! this scheme
These two days has been meat and drink to me.
Far more than we have lost is left us yet.
We have enough; I wish indeed that I
Were younger; but this hope is a good hope.
Make ready Luke's best garments, of the best
Buy for him more, and let us send him forth
To-morrow, or the next day, or to-night:
If he could go, the boy should go to-night."

Here Michael ceased, and to the fields went forth
With a light heart. The housewife for five days
Was restless morn and night, and all day long
Wrought on with her best fingers to prepare
Things needful for the journey of her son.
But Isabel was glad when Sunday came
To stop her in her work; for, when she lay
By Michael's side, she through the last two nights
Heard him, how he was troubled in his sleep:
And when they rose at morning she could see
That all his hopes were gone. That day at noon
She said to Luke, while they two by themselves
Were sitting at the door, "Thou must not go:
We have no other child but thee to lose,
None to remember—do not go away,
For if thou leave thy father he will die."
The youth made answer with a jocund voice:
And Isabel, when she had told her fears,
Recovered heart. That evening her best fare
Did she bring forth, and all together sat
Like happy people round a Christmas fire.

With daylight Isabel resumed her work;
And all the ensuing week the house appeared
As cheerful as a grove in spring: at length
The expected letter from their kinsman came,
With kind assurances that he would do
His utmost for the welfare of the boy;
To which requests were added, that forthwith
He might be sent to him. Ten times or more
The letter was read over; Isabel
Went forth to show it to the neighbours round;
Nor was there at that time on English land
A prouder heart than Luke's. When Isabel
Had to her house returned, the old man said,
"He shall depart to-morrow." To this word
The housewife answered, talking much of things
Which if at such short notice he should go,
Would surely be forgotten. But at length
She gave consent, and Michael was at ease.

Near the tumultuous brook of Green-head Ghyll,
In that deep valley, Michael had designed

To build a sheepfold; and, before he heard
The tidings of his melancholy loss,
For this same purpose he had gathered up
A heap of stones, which by the streamlet's edge
Lay thrown together, ready for the work.
With Luke that evening thitherward he walked;
And soon as they had reached the place he stopped.
And thus the old man spake to him:—"My son,
To-morrow thou wilt leave me: with full heart
I look upon thee, for thou art the same
That wert a promise to me ere thy birth,
And all thy life hast been my daily joy.
I will relate to thee some little part
Of our two histories: 'twill do thee good
When thou art from me; even if I should speak
Of things thou canst not know of.——After thou
First cam'st into the world—as oft befals
To new-born infants—thou didst sleep away
Two days, and blessings from thy father's tongue
Then fell upon thee. Day by day passed on,
And still I loved thee with increasing love.
Never to living ear came sweeter sounds
Than when I heard thee by our own fireside
First uttering, without words, a natural tune;
When thou, a feeble babe, didst in thy joy
Sing at thy mother's breast. Month followed month,
And in the open fields my life was passed,
And on the mountains, else I think that thou
Had'st been brought up upon thy father's knees.
But we were playmates, Luke: among these hills,
As well thou know'st in us, the old and young
Have played together, nor with me didst thou
Lack any pleasure which a boy can know."
Luke had a manly heart; but at these words
He sobbed aloud. The old man grasped his hand,
And said, "Nay, do not take it so: I see
That these are things of which I need not speak.
Even to the utmost I have been to thee
A kind and a good father; and herein
I but repay a gift which I myself
Received at others' hands; for, though now old
Beyond the common life of man, I still

Remember them who loved me in my youth.
Both of them sleep together: here they lived,
As all their forefathers had done; and when
At length their time was come, they were not loth
To give their bodies to the family mould.
I wish that thou shouldst live the life they lived:
But 'tis a long time to look back, my son,
And see so little gain from threescore years.
These fields were burthened when they came to me;
Till I was forty years of age, not more
Than half of my inheritance was mine.
I toiled and toiled: God bless'd me in my work,
And till these three weeks past the land was free.
It looks as if it never could endure
Another master. Heaven forgive me, Luke,
If I judge ill for thee, but it seems good
That thou shouldst go." At this the old man paused;
Then pointing to the stones near which they stood,
Thus, after a short silence, he resumed:
"This was a work for us, and now, my son,
It is a work for me; but lay one stone
Here; lay it for me, Luke, with thine own hands.
Nay, boy, be of good hope; we both may live
To see a better day. At eighty-four
I still am strong and hale: do thou thy part,
I will do mine. I will begin again
With many tasks that were resigned to thee;
Up to the heights, and in among the storms,
Will I without thee go again, and do
All works which I was wont to do alone,
Before I knew thy face. Heaven bless thee, boy
Thy heart these two weeks has been beating fast
With many hopes; it should be so: yes, yes,
I knew that thou couldst never have a wish
To leave me, Luke; thou hast been bound to me
Only by links of love; when thou art gone,
What will be left to us! But I forget
My purposes. Lay now the corner-stone,
As I requested; and hereafter, Luke,
When thou art gone away, should evil men
Be thy companions, think of me, my son,
And of this moment: hither turn thy thoughts,

And God will strengthen thee: amid all fear
And all temptation, Luke, I pray that thou
Mayst bear in mind the life thy fathers lived,
Who, being innocent, did for that cause
Bestir them in good deeds. Now, fare-thee-well;
When thou return'st, thou in this place wilt see
A work which is not here—a covenant—
'Twill be between us. But, whatever fate
Befal thee, I shall love thee to the last.
And bear thy memory with me to the grave."

The shepherd ended here, and Luke stooped down,
And, as his father had requested, laid
The first stone of the sheepfold. At the sight
The old man's grief broke from him, to his heart
He pressed his son, he kissed him and wept;
And to the house together they returned.
Hushed was that house in peace, or seeming peace,
Ere the night fell; with morrow's dawn the boy
Began his journey, and when he had reached
The public way, he put on a bold face;
And all the neighbours, as he passed their doors,
Came forth with wishes and with farewell prayers,
That followed him till he was out of sight.

A good report did from their kinsman come,
Of Luke and his well-doing; and the boy
Wrote loving letters, full of wondrous news,
Which, as the housewife phrased it, were, throughout,
"The prettiest letters that were ever seen."
Both parents read them with rejoicing hearts.
So, many months passed on, and once again
The shepherd went about his daily work
With confident and cheerful thoughts; and now
Sometimes when he could find a leisure hour
He to that valley took his way, and there
Wrought at the sheepfold. Meantime Luke began
To slacken in his duty; and at length
He in the dissolute city gave himself
To evil courses; ignominy and shame
Fell on him, so that he was driven at last
To seek a hiding place beyond the seas.

There is a comfort in the strength of love;
'Twill make a thing endurable, which else
Would overset the brain, or break the heart.
I have conversed with more than one who well
Remember the old man, and what he was
Years after he had heard this heavy news.
His bodily frame had been from youth to age
Of an unusual strength. Among the rocks
He went, and still looked up upon the sun,
And listened to the wind; and, as before,
Performed all kinds of labour for his sheep,
And for the land, his small inheritance.
And to that hollow dell from time to time
Did he repair, to build the fold of which
His flock had need. 'Tis not forgotten yet,
The pity which was then in every heart
For the old man: and 'tis believed by all
That many and many a day he thither went,
And never lifted up a single stone.

There, by the sheepfold, sometimes was he seen
Sitting alone, with that his faithful dog,
Then old, beside him lying at his feet.
The length of full seven years from time to time
He at the building of this sheepfold wrought,
And left the work unfinished when he died.
Three years, or little more, did Isabel
Survive her husband: at her death the estate
Was sold, and went into a stranger's hand.
The cottage, which was named the Evening Star,
Is gone; the ploughshare has been through the ground
On which it stood; great changes have been wrought
In all the neighbourhood; yet the oak is left
That grew beside their door; and the remains
Of the unfinished sheepfold may be seen
Beside the boisterous brook of Green-head Ghyll.

THE INSCRIBED ROCKS OF WINDERMERE.

OUR boatman told us, that at a short distance on the eastern side of Windermere lake, were some inscriptions on the rocks, which were the greatest curiosities of the place. The guide-book having made no mention of them, we were the more anxious to see what they were, and were rowed ashore accordingly, at a point not far from Lowood Inn. Here we found every smooth surface afforded by the rocks—every slab on the stratified formation —covered with inscriptions, engraved with much toil, in letters varying from six to twenty or twenty-four inches in height. On one large red stone of at least ten feet square, was engraved "1833. MONEY. LIBERTY. WEALTH. PEACE;"—a catalogue of blessings very much to be desired. On another stone was the simple date "1688:" expressive enough of the engraver's political sentiments. And on another, in larger characters, "A SLAVE LANDING ON THE BRITISH STRAND, BECOMES FREE."

All the largest stones, and slabs, some of which were horizontal, others vertical, and the rest inclined at various angles, and the whole of them giving evidence that the place had formerly been a quarry, were covered with inscriptions of a like purport. The following are a few of the most striking. One immense surface of rock bore the following names, which are transcribed in the original order:—"SUN. BULWER. DRYDEN. DAVY. BURNS. SCOTT. BURDETT. GARRICK. KEMBLE. GRAY. KEAN. MILTON. HENRY BROUGHAM. JAMES WATT. PROFESSOR WILSON. DR. JENNER." To which were added the words in characters equally conspicuous, "THE LIBERTY OF THE PRESS." "MAGNA CHARTA." This slab was a testimony, apparently, of the engraver's admiration of great intellect. One close alongside side of it was of a different style, and bore the date "1836," followed by the words, "WILLIAM IV. PRESIDENT JACKSON. LOUIS PHILIPPE. BRITANNIA RULES THE WAVES." Next to that again was a still larger surface of rock on which was indented, "NATIONAL DEBT, £800,000,000. O SAVE MY COUNTRY, HEAVEN! GEORGE III. AND WILLIAM PITT." "MONEY IS THE SINEW OF WAR." "FIELD MARSHAL WELLINGTON. HEROIC ADMIRAL NELSON. CAPTAIN COOK. ADMIRAL RODNEY." One stone, at least eight feet square, bore but one word in letters a yard long, and that was significant enough—viz. "STEAM."

On inquiring of the boatman who it was that had expended so much labour, he pointed out another stone, on which were the words, "John Longmire, Engraver," and informed us that it was a person of that name, who had spent about six years of his prime in this work—labouring here alone, and in all weathers—and both by night and by day. He took great pleasure in the task; and was, as the boatman took pains to impress upon us, rather "dull" at the time. This phrase, as he afterwards explained, implies, in this part of the country, that he was deranged; and I thought, when looking with renewed interest upon these mementos of his ingenuity and perseverance, misapplied though they were, that it was a happy circumstance that an afflicted creature could have found solace under calamity, in a manner so harmless. There was a method in the work, and a sense, too, in the poor man's ideas, which showed that his sympathies were in favour of the moral and intellectual advancement of mankind; and that, amid the last feeble glimmerings of his own reason, he could do honour to those whose intellect had benefited and adorned our age. I could learn no further particulars of him; our friend, the boatman, not being able to say whether he were dead or alive, or whether his "dullness" had ever manifested itself in a more disorderly manner than in these inscriptions.

EDGAR, THE LORD OF ENNERDALE.

A TRADITION OF WOTOBANK, NEAR EGREMONT.

IN the neighbourhood of Egremont, there is a romantic hill called Wotobank, with which a traditionary story is connected, and from which its name is said to have originated. The tale relates that "a lord of Egremont, with his lady Edwina and servants, was hunting the wolf; during the chase, the lady was missing, and after a long and painful search, her body was found lying on this romantic acclivity, or bank, mangled by a wolf, which was in the very act of ravenously tearing it to pieces. The sorrow of the husband, in the first transports of his grief, was expressed by the words—"Wo to this bank!"—whence the hill obtained the name of "Wotobank." Mrs. Cowley has adopted this legend for the subject of her beautiful poem "Edwina." After ascending Skiddaw, and casting a glance around:—

"Here—across the tangley dells;
There—on the misty distant fells,"

the poetess thus proceeds:—

—"But chiefly, Ennerdale, to thee I turn,
And o'er thy healthful vales heart-rended mourn!
—For ah! those plains, those vales, those sheltering woods,
Nourish'd by Bassenthwaite's contiguous floods,
Once witness'd such a sad and heavy deed
As makes the aching memory recede."

Then introducing the Lord of Ennerdale, she continues:—

"He, the sole heir of Atheling was known,
Whose blood, stern Scotland! 'midst thy heaths has flown.
Not five and twenty summers o'er his head
Had led their orbs, when he preferr'd to wed
The sweet Edwina. Blooming were the charms
Which her fond father gave to Henry's arms.
Long had he woo'd the charming, bashful maid,
Who, yet to listen to Love's tales afraid,
By many modest arts—(so Love ordains)
Increas'd his passion, though increas'd his pains.
At length the nuptial morn burst from the sky,
Bidding prismatic light before her fly;
Soft purple radiance streamed around her car,

Absorbing all the beams of everystar;—
Roses awaken'd as she pass'd along,
And the high lark perform'd his soaring song,
Whilst pinks, their fragrance shaking on the air,
The proud carnation's glories seem'd to share;
The breezes snatch'd their odours as they flew,
And gave them in their turn pellucid dew,
Which fed their colours to a higher tone,
Till all the earth a vegetative rainbow shone.

Beneath her husband's roof the matchless fair
Graced each delight, and each domestic care.
Her plastic needle bade fresh flow'rets grow;
And, hung in rich festoons, around her glow;
In cooling grots her shellwork seized the eye,
With skill arrang'd, to show each meltingdye;
Her taste the garden everywhere sustain'd,
In each parterre her vivid fancy reign'd.
Submissive yews in solid walls she form'd,
Or bade them rise a castle, yet unstorm'd;
In love the eagle hover'd o'er its nest,
Or seem'd a couchant lion sunk to rest.
Her husband's sports his lov'd Edwina shar'd,
For her the hawking party was prepar'd;
She roused the wolf—the foaming boar she chased,
And Danger's self was in her presence graced.

Thus roll'd two years on flowery wheels along,
Midst calm domestic bliss, and sport, and song.
O, Edgar! from pernicious Gallia's shore,
Hadst thou, immoral youth! return'd nomore,
Such years tho' lengthen'd time had sweetly run,
Down to the faintest beams of life's last sun.
But thou returnd'st! and thy voluptuous heart,
Which from temptation never knew to start,
Seized on Edwina as a lawful prize—
All dead to Honour's voice, and Conscience' secret cries.

Edgar to Ennerdale oft bent his way,
His form was courtly, and his manners gay;
To Henry he would speak of wars he'd seen,
Of tournaments, and gaudes, 'midst peace serene.
When for Edwina's ear the tale was fram'd

The beauties of bright Gallia's court were nam'd,
Their lives, their loves, all past before her view,
And many things were feign'd he never knew.
At length the prudent fair remark'd the style,
And saw beneath his ease distorted guile;—
For virtue in his tales ne'er found a place,
Nor maiden vigilance, nor matron grace,
But wild and loose his glowing stories ran,
And thus betray'd the black designing man.
As when, in eastern climes, 'midst hours of play,
A sweet boy (wand'ring at the close of day,
Along the margin of a gadding stream,
Whilst Hope around him throws her fairy dream)
Sudden beholds the panther's deadly eye,
And turns, by impulse strong, his step to fly—
So turn'd Edwina, when she saw, reveal'd,
The net th' ensnaring youth had hop'd conceal'd:
Whenever he appear'd her air grew cold,
And awed to mute despair this baron bold;
He by degrees forbore to seek her gate,
Who sat enshrin'd within, in Virtue's state.
But his wild wishes did not cease to rage,
Nor did he strive their fever to assuage—
For sinful love is ever dear to sin,
Its victims self-correction ne'er begin;
But, hurried on by hell, pursue their road,
Nor heed surrounding woes, nor tremble at their God!

The huntsman blew his horn, ere listless day
Had from his shoulder thrown his robe of gray,
Ere he had shaken from his shining hair
The rosy mists which irrigate the air.
Lord Henry heard—and from his pillow sprung,
And bold responsive notes he cheerily sung;
Then, "Wake my love!" the happy husband cried,
To her, who, sweetly slumbering at his side,
Wish'd still, thus slumbering, to wear the morn,
And almost chid the tyrant horn—
Yet quick she rose, and quick her busy maids,
Folding her yellow locks in careless braids,
Equipp'd her for the field—sweeping she flew,
Like a slim arrow from the graceful yew.

Her jet-black steed more lively seem'd to bound,
When the light burden on his back he found—
The jet-black steed her husband had bestow'd,
When first, a huntress, at his side she rode;
Long was his streaming main, his eye of fire,
Proved his descent from no ignoble sire;
He sprung 'midst Araby's far distant plains,
Whose sands the bleeding violet never stains.
And now the day in all his glories drest,
Seem'd at the bugle's call to shake off rest.
He pour'd his beams around in ample floods—
Rivers of light descended on the woods;
The plains, the valleys drank the radiantshower,
Each plant received it, and each gentle flower.
The Hunt inspir'd, the ambient æther rent
With varied sounds, as their keen course they bent:
The dogs, deep-mouth'd, in chorus form'd the cry,
And sent their forest greetings to the sky;
The horn's full tone swell'd each pervading note,
And harmony and joy around the country float.

At length a boar, thro' a dark coppice side,
Amidst the rustling bushes seem'd to glide;
Cautious he moved, like a fell thief of night,
Strung by his fears to unintended flight.
Close to the earth he softly crept along,
And shrubs, and underwood around him throng;
But ah! in vain he creeps, the air so thin,
Catches th' effluvia from his reeking skin,
The titillations to the hounds' keen nostrils fly,
Who instantly the brown recesses try.
When turn'd before them into open view,
Quick transports from each bosom flew;
The huntsman's law the churning savage found,
They suffer'd his escape twelve roods of ground,
Ere loose was let the eager mad'ning pack,
To follow in the bristly monster's track;
At length in close pursuit they pouralong,
Urged or retarded by their Leader's thong.
O'er hills, through brakes, he led them many an hour,
Straining each nerve—exhausting ev'ry power:
Now hears the dogs' faint mouthings far behind,

Then scents them as around a beck they wind—
With dread and joy alternately is fill'd
Now high with hope, and now with terror chill'd;
Then in despair he turns to meet the foe,
And rage and madness in his eyeballs glow—
When Henry, darting on before the rest,
Fix'd the bright lance within his heaving breast,
His struggling breast convulsive motions strain,
His spouting veins the foaming coursers stain:
The death-notes issue from the brazen horn,
And from th' enormous trunk the head is torn.
Straight with the tusk-arm'd head upon his spear,
Lord Henry turn'd to Her—for ever dear!
To lay the bleeding trophy at her feet,
And make his triumph more sincerely sweet—
But horror! no Edwina could be seen,
Nor on the hill's soft slope, or pasture green;
Not shelter'd, near the torrent's fall she lay,
Nor on the forest's edge, escaped the day,
Nor was she on the plain—the valleys too,
Gave no Edwina to the aching view.
Wonder and dread compress her husband's heart,
O'er the surrounding scene his eye-beams dart;
He moves—stands still—terror lifts up his hair,
He seems the pale-cheek'd spectre of despair.
And now was heard her steed's sonorous neigh,
Whose voice the rocks' firm echoes would obey;
Bounding, he comes towards them from the plain,
But his sweet mistress held no guiding rein—
The reins float loosely, as he cleft the air,
No mistress sweet, with guiding hand, was there!
From all but Henry burst terrific cries,
Silent his dread—and quite suppress'd his sighs.
His manly features sink, his eyelids close,
And all his lineaments express his woes.
Speech! O, how weak, when mighty sorrows spring,
When fears excessive to the bosom cling!
Words may to lighter troubles give a show,
But find no place where griefs transcendent grow.
At length they each a different way diverge,
Some to the mountain's haughty brow emerge,
Others pursue the plain—the wood—the dell,

Appointing where to meet, their fortune dear, to tell.

And now, O Lady! Empress of the day,
My pensive pen pursues thee on thy way!
Amidst the heat and fury of the chace,
When the fleet horsemen scarce the eye could trace.
A road succinct Edwina meant to take,
And push'd her steed across an ancient brake;
But in the thicket tangled and dismayed,
And of the thorny solitude afraid,
Again she turn'd her horse—ah! turn'd in vain,
She miss'd the op'ning to the neighb'ring plain.
At length dismounting, tremblingly she strove,
To force a path, through briars thickly wove;
The horse releas'd, straight vanish'd from her eye,
And o'er opposing brambles seem'd to fly—
The distant hounds his prick'd-up ears invade,
And quick he skims o'er ev'ry glen and glade.
His mistress, thus forsook, with prickles torn,
And weeping oft with pain, and all forlorn,
At length achiev'd a path, and saw a rill,
To which she mov'd, her ruby mouth to fill;—
Her taper'd hand immers'd beneath the stream,
Flash'd through the glassy wave with pearly gleam,
It bore the living moisture to her lips,
And eagerly the panting beauty sips,
The shining freshness o'er her brow she threw,
And bless'd the current as it sparkling flew;
Then on its borders sought a short repose,
Whilst round her, doddergrass, and pansies rose.
Sleep soon, unbidden, caught her in his snare,
And folded in his arms the weary fair,
Two aspen trees in one smooth bark were bound,
And threw a thin and trembling shadow round,
The waters gently tinkled as they fell,
And a near sheep sustained a silvery bell,
Whilst breezes o'er her temples softly stray'd,
And 'midst her floating ringlets, leaping, played,
Who would not wish to linger in such rest,
Where waters, shades, and sounds, make sleeping blest?
But, Powers Sublime! who tread the burning air,
And give to sainted charity your care,

Where roved ye now?—Where waved your filmy wings,
Where struck your harps their million-bearing strings?
If on Light's rays, swift shot from pole to pole,
Your essences supine you chose to roll,
Or the rich glowing tapestry to weave,
Which must the sun's retiring orb receive,
Yet still you should have left each task undone,
Fled from the glowing west—forsook the sun,
Rush'd in whole troops, nor left one sylph behind,
And all your cares to Ennerdale confined:
Clung round the aspens where Edwina slept,
And o'er her form your anxious vigils kept—
Whose slumbers long spun out their rosy dreams,
And still consoled her 'midst the noontide beams.
When a hard grasp which seized her listless hands,
Rude, snapt asunder their narcotic bands,
She started, and she found,—O! hated sight,
Close at her side the am'rous villain knight,
Who tried in specious terms his hopes to paint—
Inspir'd by ev'ry fiend, he call'd on every saint!

Surprise, at first, held mute Edwina's tongue,
And many changes on his theme he rung,
Ere she could pour her chaste, her proud disdain,
Or check with cold contempt his odious strain.
At length she spoke. So once, Judean Fair!
Thou turn'd'st upon the sober, hoary pair
Who slunk, with wanton thoughts and aspect grave,
To watch thee, rising from the gelid wave.
Insulted Virtue thunder'd from thy tongue,
And o'er thy eye indignant lightnings hung,
Swift came the vollied speech;—grand was thy tone,
And Chastity in bright effulgence shone.
Around the ivory form dark myrtles grew,
To snatch thee from the gazing monster's view;
Through their deep foliage came thy pointed words,
Thy glance was fire—thy sentences were swords!

Such were Edwina's tones, her look, her air,
Striking the young seducer with despair!
Yes, young he was, in beauty's fullest prime,
Untarnish'd yet, untouch'd by withering time!
O'er his red cheek soft dimples playful ran,

Whilst grace and sinewy strength proclaimed The man!
His charms, his passion, sweet Edwina spurned,
And with unfeigned abhorrence, stately turned;
Then walk'd with mien composed across the moor,
Though tremblings seized her heart, and doubtings sore.
But Edgar soon she heard, step quick behind,
And then to mad'ning fears her soul resigned.
She seemed to borrow from the wind its wings,
When from its southern portal first it springs—
Flying, as borne upon the billowy air,
Urged by distraction on, and blank despair.
Her base pursuer spurr'd by dire intent,
Kept closely in the track the fair one went;
Nor hurried much, but thought her failing feet
Would soon retard a course so wondrous fleet—
He thought aright, and in his felon arms,
Pressed Henry's beauteous wife, half wild with dread alarms.

Scarce had he dared to grasp her sinking frame,
When with the quickness of devouring flame,
A furious wolf from out the bordering wood
With eyes all glaring near Edwina stood—
The brindled hair rose stiff upon his chine,
Of ghastly, deathful joy, the horrid sign;
His clinging sides confessed his famished state,
And his deep howl proclaimed a victim's fate.
The coward fled!—O! now my pen forbear,
Nor with the shrieks of terror rend the air!—
The wolf's fell teeth—but O! I check the song,
Nor can the horrid, agonizing chord prolong.

The savage, starting from his bleeding prey,
Rush'd to his haunt, and briefly fled away;
Approaching steps declared swift danger nigh,
And forc'd—too late! the unglutted beast to fly.
Those steps were Henry's!—he first reached the spot,
For him to reach it, was the dreadful lot!
He saw her marble bosom torn—her mangled head;
He saw—mysterious fate! Edwina dead!
Those eyes were closed, whose rich and beamy light,
Would shed a lustre on pale Sorrow's night—
Dumb was that honied mouth, whose graceful speech,
Beyond the schoolman's eloquence would reach!

The snowy arms which lately clasped her lord,
Now streaked with flowing blood—O! thought abhorred!
Before his starting eyes, all lifeless hang,
And give him more than death's last, rending pang.
His cries of agony spread o'er the plain,
And reached the distant undulating main;
His screams of anguish struck with terror more
Than the lank wolf's most desolating roar.
Vain his attendants sooth—in vain they pray,
In stormy grief he wearied down the day.
A furious maniac now he raged around,
And tore the bushes from the embracing ground,
Then spent, all prone upon the earth he fell,
And from his eyes the gushing torrents swell;
When sorrow could articulate its grief,
When words allowed a transient short relief,
"Woe to thee, Bank!" were the first sounds that burst,
"And be thy soil with bitter offspring curst!
"Woe to thee, Bank, for thou art drunk with gore,
"The purest heart of woman ever bore!"
"Woe to thee, Bank!" the attendants echoed round,
And pitying shepherds caught the grief-fraught sound.
Thus, to this hour, through every changing age,
Through ev'ry year's still ever-varying stage,
The name remains; and Wo-to-Bank is seen,
From ev'ry mountain bleak, and valley green—
Dim Skiddaw views it from his monstrous height,
And eagles mark it in their dizzy flight;
The Bassenthwaite's soft murmurs sorrow round,
And rocks of Buttermere protect the ground,
Rills of Helvellyn raging in their fall,
Seem on Lodore's rough sympathy to call—
From peak to peak they wildly burst away,
And form, with rushing tone, a hollow, dirge-like lay.
Not rocks, and cataracts and alps alone,
Paint out the spot, and make its horrors known.
For faithful lads ne'er pass, nor tender maid,
But the soft rite of tears is duly paid;
Each can the story to the traveller tell,
And on the sad disaster, pitying dwell—
Thus Wo-to-Bank, thou'rt known thy swains among,
And now thou liv'st within an humble stranger's song!"

LADY EVA AND THE GIANT.

A LEGEND OF YEWDALE.

AS you enter the romantic vale of Yewdale, about a quarter of a mile above the saw-mills, by looking over the hedge to your right, you may perceive, near to the verge of the precipitous bank of Yewdale Beck, and a few yards from the roadside, a long narrow mound which seems to be formed of solid stone covered with moss, but which a nearer inspection would show to be composed of several blocks fitted so closely together as to prove the mound to have had an artificial, and not a natural origin. You observe it is somewhere between three and four yards long. That singular accumulation of lichen-clad rock has been known for centuries amongst the natives of Yewdale and the adjacent valleys, by the romance-suggesting designation of Girt Will's Grave. How it came by that name, and how Cauldron Dub and Yewdale Bridge came to be haunted, my task is now to tell.

Some few hundred years ago, the inhabitants of these contiguous dales were startled from their propriety, if they had any, by a report that one of the Troutbeck giants had built himself a hut, and taken up his abode in the lonely dell of the Tarns, above Yewdale Head. Of course you have read the history and exploits of the famous Tom Hickathrift, and remembering that he was raised at Troutbeck, you will not be much surprised when I tell you that it was always famous for a race of extraordinary size and strength; for even in these our own puny days, the biggest man in Westmoreland is to be found in that beautiful vale.

The excitement consequent upon the settlement of one of that gigantic race in this vicinity soon died away, and the object of it, who stood somewhere about nine feet six out of his clogs, if they were in fashion then, and was broad in fair proportion, became known to the neighbours as a capital labourer, ready for any such work as was required in the rude and limited agricultural operations of the period and locality—answered to the cognomen of "Girt (great) Will o' t' Tarns," and, once or twice, did good service as a billman under the Knight of Conistone, when he was called upon to muster his powers to assist in repelling certain roving bands of Scots or Irish, who were wont, now and again, to invade the wealthy plains of low Furness.

The particular Knight who was chief of the Flemings of Conistone, at the period of the giant's location at the Tarns, was far advanced in years, and, in addition to some six or eight gallant and stately sons, had

"One fair daughter, and no more,
The which he loved passing well."

And Eva le Fleming, called by the country people "the Lady Eva," was famed throughout the broad north for her beauty and gentleness, her high-bred dignity and her humble virtues; but it is not with her that my story has to do. She, like the mother of "the gentle lady married to the Moor," had a maid called Barbara, an especial favourite with her mistress, and, in her own sphere, deemed quite as beautiful. In fact, it was hinted that, when she happened to be in attendance upon her lady on festive or devotional occasions, the eyes of even knights and well-born squires were as often directed to the maid as to the mistress, and seemed to express as much admiration in one direction as the other.

And when mounted on the Lady Eva's own palfrey, bedecked in its gayest trappings, she rode, as she oftentimes did, to visit her parents at Skelwith, old and young were struck with her beauty, and would turn, as she ambled past, to gaze after her, and to wonder at the elegance of her figure, the ease of her deportment, and the all-surpassing loveliness of her features. Her lady, notwithstanding the disparity of their rank, loved her as a sister, and it was whispered amongst her envious fellow-servants, that her mistress's fondness made her assume airs unbecoming her station. True enough it was that she seemed sufficiently haughty and scornful in her reception of the homage paid to her charms by the young men of her own rank, and by many above it. The only one to whom she showed the slightest courtesy on these occasions was wild Dick Hawksley, the Knight's falconer, and he was also the only one who appeared to care no more for her favours than for her frowns.

The Lady Eva, as well befits high-born dames, was somewhat romantic in her tastes, and would often row for hours upon the lake, and wander for miles through the woods, or even upon the mountains, unattended, save by her favourite bower-maiden. And one evening in autumn, after having been confined for two whole days to the hall, by heavy and incessant rain, tired of playing chess with her father, and battledore with her younger brothers, or superintending the needlework of her maids, and tempted by the brilliant moonlight and now unobscured skies, she summoned Barbara, and set out upon a stroll by the lake side.

The pair were sauntering along a path cut through the dense coppice, the lady leaning in condescending affection upon the shoulder of her maiden, and listening to a recital of how, on her return from some of her visits to her parents, she had been waylaid by Great Will of the Tarns, and how on a recent evening he had attempted to seize her rein, and would have stopped her, had she not whipped the palfrey and bounded past him. The lady was expressing her indignation at this insolence, when a gigantic figure sprang upon the pathway, and, snatching up the screaming Barbara with the same ease with which she herself would have lifted an infant, vanished on the instant amongst the thick hazels.

The Lady Eva stood for a minute struck powerless with terror and astonishment at this audacious outrage; but the sound of the monster crashing his headlong course through the coppice, and the half-stifled screams of his captive, soon recalled her suspended faculties, and then

> "Fair" Eva "through the hazel-grove
> Flew, like a startled cushat dove,"

back to the hall, where, breathless with terror and exertion, she gave the alarm that Barbara had been carried off by the giant. There was noisy and instantaneous commotion amongst the carousing gentles at the upper, and the loitering lacqueys at the lower end of the hall. Dick Hawksley, and a few more, darted off in immediate pursuit on foot, while several rushed to the stables, in obedience to the call of their young masters, who were, one and all, loudly vociferating for their horses. Scarce a minute passed, ere half a dozen Flemings, attended by as many mounted followers, were spurring like lightning through the wood in the direction of Yewdale. They came in sight of the giant and his burthen as he neared Cauldron Dub, with the light-heeled falconer close behind, calling loudly upon him to stay his flight; but he held on with tremendous strides, till he reached the brow over the pool, when, finding that the horsemen were close upon him, and that it was hopeless to try to carry his prize farther, he stopped—uttered one terrible shout of rage and disappointment—and whirled his shrieking victim into the flooded beck, resuming his now unencumbered flight with increased speed.

Dick Hawksley rushed over the bank a little lower down, and the horsemen, abandoning the chase, galloped to the brink of the stream, which was high with the recent rains. They saw the falconer plunge into the torrent, as the bower maiden, yet buoyant with her light garments, was borne rapidly down. They saw him seize her with one hand, and strike out gallantly for the bank with the other, but the current was too strong for him, encumbered as he was with the girl in his grasp. The devoted pair were swept down the stream, at a rate that made the spectators put their horses to a gallop to keep them in sight, even while the exertions of the brave falconer sufficed to sustain their heads above water, which was only till they came under the bridge, where the water, pent in by the narrow arch, acquired four-fold force, and there they heard him utter a hoarse cry of despair, and the gallant Hawksley and the Lady Eva's beauteous favourite were seen no more, till their bodies were found, days after, on the shore far down the lake.

One or two of the horsemen continued to gallop down the side of the beck, in the bootless hope of being able even yet to render them some aid, but the most of them turned their horses' heads, and went off once more at their utmost speed in pursuit of the murderous giant. He, considering the chase at an end, had slackened his pace, and they were not long in overtaking him. Great Will struck out manfully with his club (time out of mind the giant's favourite weapon) as they rushed upon him, but they speedily surrounded him, and, amid a storm of vengeful yells and bitter execrations, the Giant of the Tarns was stretched upon the sward, "with the blood running like a little brook" from a hundred wounds; for he was so frightfully slashed and mangled by their swords, that, as my informant naively averred, there was not so much whole skin left upon his huge body as would have made a tobacco-pouch.

It will be apparent enough to the most obtuse intellect, that, after such events as these, the localities where they occurred must, of necessity, be haunted; and, as the ghosts of murderers, as well as of murderees, if they be right orthodox apparitions, always appear to be re-enacting the closing scene of their earthly career, it is scarcely required of me to dilate farther upon the manner of their appearance. Of course I do not expect, and certainly do not wish to be called upon to prove the even-down truth of every particular of the story, with which I have been doing my little best to amuse you; but the assured fact of the Dub and the bridge being haunted, and that by sundry most pertinacious spirits, I am ready to maintain against all comers.

KIRKBY LONSDALE BRIDGE.

A LEGEND.

NEAR to the bridge which crosses the Lune, not far from Kirkby Lonsdale, the scenery is truly romantic. The river, which is here of considerable width, winds through the bottom of the valley, and is overshadowed by the trees that grow upon its banks. Its current is roughened by the rocks which form its bed, some of which stand up in huge moss-grown blocks in the midst of the stream. The water is clear to a great depth, and the steep grassy banks, and abundance of trees which close in the prospect, give it an air of seclusion. This stream is plentifully stocked with trout and salmon, and here the angler may sit and watch the gilded fly with a devotion worthy of a Davy or a Walton.

The singular construction of the bridge renders it an object of curiosity; and when viewed in connection with the river and valley of the Lune, it forms one of the most romantic prospects on which the eye can dwell. It is composed of three beautifully ribbed arches, the centre one rising to the height of thirty-six feet above the stream. It is a lofty, firm and handsome structure, but so narrow as almost to deserve the taunt cast upon the "auld brig of Ayr:"—

"Where twa wheelbarrows trembled when they met:" at least no two carriages of a larger size can pass each other; but, for the security of the foot passengers, there are angular recesses in the battlements, corresponding with the projecting piers.

Antiquity has cast her veil over this erection, and a consequent obscurity envelopes its history. If, however, we may rely on popular tradition, the building is to be ascribed to an unmentionable personage; of whom it is said, "that he built the bridge one windy night, and that in fetching the stones from a distance, he let fall the last apronfull as he flew over a fell hard by." This gentleman has been "a bridge-builder," "time out of mind," notwithstanding the improbability of his employing "himself in works of so much real utility to men." Such an historical fact may, however, account for the huge blocks of stone found in various parts of the neighbouring moors.

"Still grand, and beautiful, and good,
Has Lonsdale bridge unshaken stood,
And scorned the swollen, raging flood,
    For many ages;
Though antiquaries, who have tried

Some date to find, in vain have pryed
In ancient pages.

Then hear what old tradition says:—
Close by the Lune in former days
Lived an old maid, queer all her ways,
In Yorkshire bred;
Though now forgot what she was named,
For cheating she was always famed,
'Tis truly said.

She had a cow, a pony too;
When o'er the Lune, upon the brow,
Had passed one night these fav'rites two,
'Twas dark and rainy;
Her cow was o'er, she knew her bellow,
Her pony too, poor little fellow,
She heard him whinny.

Alack, alack a day! she cries,
As overflowed her streaming eyes,
When lo! with her to sympathise,
Old Nick appears;
'Pray, now, good woman, don't despair,
But lay aside all anxious care,
And wipe your tears.

'To raise a bridge I will agree,
That in the morning you shall see,
But mine for e'er the first must be
That passes over;
So by these means you'll soon be able
To bring the pony to his stable,
The cow her clover.'

In vain were sighs and wailings vented,
So she at last appeared contented,
It was a bargain, she consented,
For she was Yorkshire;
Now home she goes in mighty glee,
Old Satan, too, well pleased he,
Went to his work, Sir.

When Ilus' son surrounded Troy
With walls that nothing might destroy,

Two gods some time he did employ,
    But never paid 'em;
Here Satan, certain of his prize,
With building made a desp'rate noise,
    So fast he laid on.

In short, the morning streaks appear,
The bridge is built and Satan there,
When this old lady now drew near,
    Her lap-dog with her;
'Behold the bridge,' the tempter cries,
'Your cattle, too, before your eyes,
    So hie you thither.'

But mark! she well the bargain knew,
A bun then from her pocket drew,
And showed it first to little Cue,
    Then overthrew it;
Now flew the bun, now ran the dog,
For eager was the mangy rogue,
    Nor stood to view it.

'Now, crafty Sir, the bargain was,
That you should have what first did pass
Across the bridge, so now, alas!
    The dog's your right,'
The cheater cheated, struck with shame,
Squinted and grinned, then in a flame
    He vanished quite."

THE SPECTRE ARMY.

A WEIRD TALE OF SOUTRA FELL.

SOUTER FELL, or Soutra Fell as it is sometimes called, is a considerable mountain situated to the eastward of Skiddaw and Blencathara. The west and north sides are barricaded with steep rocks, apparently 900 yards in height, and everywhere difficult of access.

A very remarkable phenomenon has exhibited itself on this mountain, which, though difficult to account for satisfactorily, is too well authenticated by numerous spectators to be discredited. We allude to the appearance of troops of visionary horsemen, crossing the mountains, advancing, retreating, and performing different military evolutions—an optical delusion which has been observed in this vicinity, to the great astonishment of the rustics of the vale.

> "As when a shepherd of the Hebrid isles
> Placed far amid the melancholy main
> (Whether it be lone fancy him beguiles,
> Or that aërial beings sometimes deign
> To stand, embodied, to our senses plain),
> Sees on the naked hill or valley low,
> The whilst in ocean Phœbus dips his wain,
> A vast assembly moving to and fro;
> Then all at once in air dissolves the wondrous show."
>
> THOMSON.

The following account of this singular appearance, which is scarcely paralleled in history, is contained in Hutchison's History of Cumberland, the particulars being collected by Mr. Smith, who observes that he went himself to examine the spectators, who asserted the facts very positively. "On midsummer eve, 1735, a servant in the employ of William Lancaster, of Blakehills, about half a mile from Souterfell, related that he saw the east side of the mountain, towards the summit, covered with a regular marching army for above an hour together. They consisted of distinct bodies of troops, which appeared to proceed from an eminence in the north end, and marched over a niche in the top, marked A and B in the sketch given in the above work; but as no other person in the neighbourhood had seen a similar appearance, he was discredited and laughed at.

"Two years after, on midsummer eve also, between the hours of eight and nine, William Lancaster himself imagined that several gentlemen were following their horses at a distance, as if they had been hunting; and taking them for such, paid no regard to it, till about ten minutes after, again turning his head towards the place, they appeared to be mounted, and a vast army following, five in rank, crowding over at the same place, where the servant said he saw them two years before. He then called his family, who all agreed in the same opinion; and what was most extraordinary, he frequently observed that some one of the five would quit the ranks, and seem to stand in a fronting posture, as if he was observing and regulating the order of their march, or taking account of the numbers, and after some time appeared to return full-gallop to the station he had left, which they never failed to do as often as they quitted their lines, and the figure that did so was generally one of the middlemost men in the rank. As it grew later, they seemed more regardless of discipline, and rather had the appearance of people riding from a market, than an army, though they continued crowding on, and marching off, as long as there was light to see them."

This phenomenon was no more observed till the remarkably serene midsummer evening which preceded the last Scotch rebellion. The parties who had witnessed it on the previous occasion, having been much ridiculed for their report, were determined to call a greater number of witnesses of this strange phenomenon; and having first observed it rigidly, and with great caution themselves, and being fully assured they were not deceived as to the actual appearances, they convened about twenty-six persons from different places in the neighbourhood to bear testimony to the existence of the fact. These all affirmed, and attested before a magistrate, that they saw a similar appearance to that just described, but not conducted with the same regularity, having also the appearance of carriages interspersed. The numbers of the troops were incredible, for they filled lengthways nearly half a mile, and continued so in a brisk march for above an hour, and would probably have done so much longer had not the darkness of approaching night intervened.

> "Anon appears a brave, a gorgeous show
> Of horsemen shadows, moving to and fro.
>
> * * * * *
>
> Silent the visionary warriors go,
> Wending in ordered pomp their upward way,
> Till the last banner of the long array
> Had disappeared, and every trace is fled
> Of splendour—save the beacon's spiry head,
> Tipt with eve's latest gleam of burning red."
>
> WORDSWORTH.

The horse and man, upon strict looking at, appeared to be but one being, rather than two distinct ones, but they did not at all resemble clouds or vapours of any kind.

William Lancaster observed that he never considered these aërial images to be real beings, because of the impracticability of a march over the precipices they seemed to traverse, where horses' hoofs had never trod before. They did not, however, appear to be any less real than on the former occasion; for so convinced were the spectators of the reality of what they had seen, that, as soon as the sun had dawned next morning, several of them climbed the mountain, through an idle expectation of finding the marks of horses' feet, after so numerous an army; but when they arrived at the supposed scene of action, not the mark of a single hoof was discernible, nor have any tidings been received of troops being in the neighbourhood up to this time.[6]

Though this part of the country, like every other, where cultivation has been lately introduced, abounds in all the *aniles fabellæ* of fairies, ghosts, and apparitions, these are never even fabled to have been seen by more than one or two persons at a time, and the view is always said to be momentary. But in this case the twenty-six spectators saw all alike the same changes, and at the same time, as they discovered by asking each other questions as any change took place. Nor was this wonderful phenomenon observed by these individuals only; it was seen by every person, at every cottage, for a mile round; neither was it confined to a momentary view; for, from the time it was first observed, the appearance must have lasted at least two hours and a half, viz., from half-past seven, till the night coming on prevented the further view; nor yet was the distance such as could impose rude resemblances on the eyes of credulity. The whole story has certainly much of the air of a romance, and it may appear to some fittest for Amadis de Gaul, or Glenville's System of Witches, than for insertion here as a fact. But although it may be difficult to reconcile its probability, and beyond even philosophy to explain, yet such is the evidence we have of its occurrence, that I do not myself entertain the slightest doubt of its having actually taken place as here related. The whole, however, was unquestionably an optical delusion.

As instances have frequently occurred in which the forms and action of human beings have been pictured in the clouds, or in vapour, it seems highly probable, on a consideration of all the circumstances of the case, that certain vapours must have hovered round the mountain when these appearances were observed. It is also possible that these vapours may have been impressed with the shadowy forms which seemed to "imitate humanity," by a particular operation of the sun's rays, united with some singular, but unknown, refractive combination then taking place in the atmosphere.

It has been remarked that these appearances were observed most particularly on the eve of the last Scotch Rebellion, when troops of horsemen might be privately exercising at no great distance. Indeed, the Editor of the *Lonsdale Magazine*, without giving his authority, observes, that it was afterwards actually discovered "to have been the rebels exercising on the western coast of Scotland, whose movements had been reflected by some fine transparent vapour similar to the Fata Morgana."[7]

Instances are recorded of the phenomena of spectral armies having been occasionally witnessed in other localities. It has been stated that a troop of phantom horsemen was seen coursing over the heights of Helvellyn the day before the battle of Marston Moor.[8] Hutchinson, in his *History of Cumberland*, relates the following as a parallel instance with that of Soutra Fell. In the spring of 1707, early in a serene morning, was observed by two persons in Leicestershire an appearance of an army marching along, till going behind a great hill it disappeared. The forms of pikes, and carbines were distinguishable; the march was not entirely in one direction, but was at the first like the junction of two armies, and the meeting of generals.[9] There is also a well-authenticated statement of a similar phenomenon, witnessed not long ago, on the Mendip Hills, in Somersetshire;[10] and Speed tells us of something of a like nature as preceding a dreadful intestine war.[11] Something of this kind may have given rise to Ossian's grand and awful mythology.

These optical illusions, occurring on Soutra Fell, form a subject peculiarly adapted for "the poet's pen," and are finely illustrated in the following poem, written in conformity with the popular belief of the lake villagers, that it really was a presentiment of the Scotch Rebellion, and that the horrors of the final battle were depicted in a prophetic manner. There can be no impiety in supposing, as this happened immediately before that rebellion which was intended to subvert the liberty, the law, and the religion of England, that though immediate prophecies may have ceased, these visionary beings might be directed to warn mankind of approaching tumults.

"Look how the world's poor people are amazed
At apparitions, signs, and prodigies,
Whereon with fearful eyes they long have gazed,
Infusing them with dreadful prophecies."

Shakespeare's *Venus and Adonis.*

A VISIONARY TALE OF THE SCOTCH REBELLION.

While yet I gazed on Soutra's fell,
A sight appeared (I live and tell!),
Strange, ominous, and yet obscure,
But fate has wrought the vision sure;
Too soon explained, it bodes no good,

But desolation marks, and blood,
I saw at once in full career
Equestrian troops dire-armed appear,
Descending swift the mountains steep
No earthly steed could footstep keep;
Yet many hundreds were their might.
The glitt'ring stars revealed the sight—
Lightnings, forbidding to conceal,
Burst, 'midst drawn swords and helmets' steel.
On me when burst their dreadful gleam
Faint my sunk soul emits a scream;
And Walter Selby thus began—
(Walter still less, or more than man)
Shouting till every echo round
The mountain nymphs appalled resound;
"Saw ever man such gallant sight?
A thousand steeds on Soutra's height,
Its fierce descent—in martial pride
A thousand riders stem its side,
With managed pride and daring front!
What mortal force shall bide their brunt?
See how they gallop down yon rock!—
What mortal eye can bear the shock?
The roe of Soutra's lightest bound
Shrinks from the delvy deep profound,
Where not the falcon strains her flight
Above the eagled eyrey's height.
O, for a steed so sure and swift
That might me with these horsemen lift—
These airy knights! My wanton brown,
Famed far and wide for fleet renown,
That darts o'er Derwent like a bird,
Matched with such palfrey and its lord
With wonder froze, its progress slow,
Would think the Derwent ceased to flow.
Ne'er gossamer in summer race
So swift, so sylphy held the chace.
Alarm in every village dwells,
For we all know what this foretells—
A battle lost, a ruined cause.
I heard my father say there was
Then seen on dread Helvellyn's side

An armed host like this to ride:
Yet difference marked—beneath a crown
The eye of royalty there frowns;
A regal glaive, like mailed Mars,
That streams a meteor thro' the wars,
Points at their head to Marston Moor,
Soon to be drenched with British gore.
On those whose standard new unfurls,
Menace the coronets of earls;
The wode weird sisters waft each count,
And thanes ride wild at their surmount.
"Now Heav'n's right hand protect us!" cried
The dame that shares stern Wilton's pride;
(Once bride of Grey, for beauty famed,
And oft for boast of lineage named;
But now her blood, by age grown cold,
Yet tumult's in her mortal mould);
"What evils shall I yet sustain!
Portentous scene—terrific train!
What follows these?" with instant breath
The pedlar cries; "misfortune—death:
To many, misery—death, to some—
Some who are present, sure will come
Death sudden, early—"

"Cease thy croak,
Thou northern raven," Walter spoke;
"If they are phantoms, let them pass—
For men of mist what care e'er was
In constant souls; if flesh and bone,
(Such by their bearing are alone
This gallant band) as I believe,
As such I greet them and receive,
Good, gallant soldiers for our King—
For them shall then the welkin ring."
No sooner said, but seized his horn;
Around the mountain echoes borne
Resounds the bugle far and wide.
The spectred steedmen then descried
A mile's full quarter, seem'd to halt;
The youth again, with lips at fault,
Seized mad the ill-directed horn;
His hand the pedlar seized with scorn;

"Unhallowed, dare not thus deride
What heaven's all pregnant powers confide,
For man's instruction is this vision sent;"
(With that the bugle from his hand he rent);
"Young gentleman, be wise, be ruled:"
The lost musician stood in silence school'd.
The shadowy troops with sword and lance,
And martial pride elate, advance;
Within a hundred yards they seem;
Terrific now their hauberks gleam—
As dazzling more than mortal sight.
Yet 'midst my trance of wild affright,
I marked them, as along they went,
And living forms as such they meant,
I then imagined that I knew
Of many men in dreadful hue—
Death's pale discolour—doomed the ghost to yield,
Instance exact to perish in the field,
Or in cold blood to wait their doom—
The scaffold's fate—without a tomb;
Pride of the Stuart's strength, nor unallied,
In blood, that Brunswick's happier host defied;
The Maxwells, Boyds, Drummonds, and Gordons famed,
Scots, Ogilvies, Camerons, Foresters, high named!
One youth there was—for now the battle raged,
A band more powerful, vengeance nigh presaged,
A fierce assault proclaims the adverse power—
One youth there was, amidst destruction's lour,
Turned still the stream and every foe defied,
Oft raised his arm, and oft in blood 'twas dyed;
And, as his faint companions fell, he stood
Erect in arms, and drenched in hostile blood;
At last his prowess sunk—a falchion keen
Light' on his helmet, and burst the warrior's screen;
Then, as he fell, a visage too well known
Burst on my view, with death's stern front though prone,
'Twas Selby's self—his dread eidolon's form,
Like Brutus threatened in Philippi's storm.
Selby looked thunderstruck with wild amaze,
But mortal eye could not abide the gaze.
He sunk, forestalled the agonies of death,
And on the ground suspended was his breath;

His horn then sounds the melody of woe,
Some few sad notes that reach the issue's flow,
E're the seer's hand had checked his purpose bold;
Such notes the furies whilsom did unfold,
When Plato gave to Proserpine his hand,
And love stood awed, nor dared his force withstand
The tyrant's force—we wait all frenzied o'er,
And Selby yet alive, as dead, deplore.

All this was horror, but how faint the view
To what too soon all real must ensue,
Shall I relate how sunk each noble name?
Too well 'tis known in blasts of hideous fame;
In prose 'tis written, and in verse 'tis strung,
And songs funereal the dire dirge have sung.
The ruined castle, and the prostrate hall,
The exile's wand'ring, and the hero's fall;
Sons unattainted, sires suspicion haunts,
And childless sires their offspring's exit taunts;
Where such is heard in lamentation's air,
And more sunk deep in silence of despair;
Feelings of family perpetual burn,
And tears incessant fill the nation's urn.
Such was the scene ere dire Culloden's plain
The northern ravens glutted with the slain;
Nor rested then, for in the ebon car
The dire Erynnis of fell civil war
Held yoked her dark steeds from the fatal field,
A part succeeded reckless yet to yield,
With colours flying, and the pibroch's sound,
As if they scorned the violated ground,
As vengeance filled their bosoms fraught with ire,
As if they sought a respite to retire,
On adverse fortune scorned to waste their strength,
But thought calamity would reach its length;
Then, to return—but nobler thoughts evince,
Convinced by reason they salute their Prince,
Convinced, revere the majesty of laws,
Nor wreck their fortunes in a desperate cause;
'Twas thus each fought with still undaunted heart,
And each 'twas thought maintained the better part.

Now civil war has spent its savage rage,

Say, shall we now for anarchy engage?
Exhaust all purpose of heaven-granted life,
For no one purpose but the love of strife.
Rather than that, let's seek the pristine Cain,
Or rather seek with Lamech's force to reign,
Lamech, than Cain, the seven times told more curs'd,
For even Cain was not yet found the worst.
Then check this brutal rage, while yet there's power,
While yet the monster's something to devour;
While not by treason borne, to ruin hurled,
Stands in its frame the firm majestic world.

Another curious and interesting phenomenon was once observed on Souter Fell, somewhat differing from that already described, though probably resulting from the same combined causes. "One summer evening, in the year 1743, the servant of Mr. Wren, of Wilton Hall, was sitting at the door with his master, when they both saw the figure of a man with a dog, pursuing some horses along the mountain side, a place so steep that a horse could scarcely keep his footing upon it. These visionary forms appeared to run at an amazing pace, till they got out of sight at the lower end of the Fell. Mr. Wren and his servant next morning ascended the steep mountain, expecting to find the man dead, being persuaded he must be killed in galloping at so furious a rate; but to their surprise, they found not a shoe, nor even any vestige whatever of man, dog, or horse."[12] This story they sometime concealed; at length, however, they ventured to relate it, and were (as might be expected), heartily laughed at.

Nearly allied to this is another atmospheric phenomenon, occasionally seen among the mountains, though of rare occurrence. It consists of an aërial figure, depicted on a dense or misty atmosphere, not unfrequently assuming a grotesque or highly magnified appearance. The same phenomenon has been observed amongst the Scotch mountains. Mr. Smith, M.P. for Norwich, witnessed it in ascending Ben Nevis. On the crown of that mountain there is a crater-like hollow, in which was a misty vapour. In the midst of this appeared a human figure in motion. Mr. Smith held up his hands, and the figure did the same.[13]

This appearance is most rationally explained on the principles of refraction and reflection, the shadowy form being no other than the image of a reality, favourably posited with relation to the refracting medium and the observer's eye. This man-in-the-mist was doubtless the shadow of the real man, created by his coming between the vapour and the sun; yet perhaps the aërial beings that have been said to people the Highland mountains, may be traced to some such origin.

The appearance of the Spectre of the Broken, an aërial figure which is sometimes seen amongst the Hartz mountains of Hanover, may be accounted for in the same manner. The following is an interesting account of this phenomenon by M. Hane:—"Having ascended the Broken Mountain," says he, "for the thirtieth time, I was at length so fortunate as to have the pleasure of seeing this phenomenon. The sun rose about four o'clock, and the atmosphere being quite serene towards the east, its rays could pass without any obstruction over the Heinrichshöhe mountain. In the south-west, however, towards the mountain Achtermannshöhe, a brisk west wind carried before it thin transparent vapours. About a quarter-past four I looked round, to see whether the atmosphere would permit me to have a free prospect to the south-west, when I observed, at a very great distance towards the Achtermannshöhe, a human figure of a monstrous size! A violent gust of wind having almost carried away my hat, I clapped my hand to it: and in moving my arm towards my head, the colossal figure did the same.

"The pleasure which I felt at this discovery can hardly be described; for I had already walked many a weary step in the hope of seeing this shadowy image, without being able to gratify my curiosity. I immediately made another movement, by bending my body, and the colossal figure before me repeated it. I was desirous of doing the same thing once more, but my colossus had vanished. I remained in the same position, waiting to see whether it would return; and in a few minutes it again made its appearance on the Achtermannshöhe. I then called the landlord of the neighbouring inn, and having both taken the position which I had taken alone, we looked towards the Achtermannshöhe, but did not perceive anything. We had not, however, stood long, when two such colossal figures were formed over the above eminence, which repeated their compliments, by bending their bodies as we did, after which they vanished. We retained our position, kept our eyes fixed on the spot, and in a little time the two figures again stood before us, and were joined by a third," that of a traveller who then came up and joined the party. "Every movement made by us these figures imitated; but with this difference, that the phenomenon was sometimes weak and faint, sometimes strong and well defined."[14]

RUSTIC POETS OF THE LAKE DISTRICT.

JOHN OLDLAND AND JAMIE MUCKELT.

AMONG the various traits of local character in the English Lake district, there is not perhaps, one more amusing than that propensity to rhyming which a number of individuals has exhibited, in all the rustic grace of native ignorance. A few instances of this nature can only be admitted within the limited compass of these pages, but they will not be without their interest to those who feel a pleasure in tracing the unassisted efforts of natural genius.

John Oldland was an inhabitant of Crosthwaite, existing about the beginning of the last century. His propensity to rhyming was such, that many of his rhymes, as they are provincially called, are still repeated by the older inhabitants of the neighbourhood. A few, and but a few of these rhymes, we shall here insert.

When he attended Ulverston market, as he generally did, he put up at the Dog, in Dalton Gate, then kept by Betty Woodburn and her husband, though now gone and forgotten. Audland, as he was called, was so much addicted to rhyming, that he did it on all occasions with various success; the following, though still remembered, is one of his clumsy attempts:—Calling one Thursday at the public-house door with some other farmers, the landlord replied in his politest manner, "Coming, Sir." On which Audland, looking up at the sign, observed:—

"This dog he runs wi' his tail to the south,
But co' on the landlord, an' he'll gi' mouth."

Once when his landlady, at the Dog, had urged him to clear off a long score, which he had run up at the house, he gave her the following promissory note, which was accepted:—

"I, John Oldland,
  Befoar I gang hence,
Owe Betty Woodburn
  Just six and two pence.
An', Thursday come sennet,
  I'll pay off the auld scoar,
An' wha knas but I may
  Spend twice as mich moar."

The smartest of John's rhymes was made on the occasion of his being put to trouble (as it is properly termed in the provincial dialect) by a lawyer, for some debt which he had incurred at Ulverston; a proof that not only poets, but all who meddle with rhyme, are poor. John repeated with emphasis—

> "God mead men,
> An' men mead money;
> God mead bees,
> An' bees mead honey;
> But the D—l mead lawyers an' tornies,
> An' pleac'd 'em at U'ston and Daltan i' Forness."

We shall only have room to notice another of these "rustic bards." He too was a Crosthwaite man, but of a more recent date. We do not intend to insinuate that there is any predisposing cause about Crosthwaite, that inclines the inhabitants to rhyme, but it happens that we remember these two at the present moment; by an association of ideas, the one has probably conjured up the other.

Jamie Muckelt was undoubtedly the best rhymer in that part of the country; and, consequently his rhymes have been more carefully preserved than those of any other. We have room, however, for only a few specimens.

Jamie was a farmer; and once, returning from the market he had overset, or, as he called it, capsized the cart. His wife was angry, and eagerly inquired the cause of such an accident. Jamie, with that *sang froid* for which he was so remarkable, only replied,

> "Caerlessly, thou may depend—
> Pooin' away at t' helter end."

A common footpath led through a field in which Jamie had a crop of pease one year. These held out a temptation, Jamie considered, to passengers to be taking tithe in kind. To prevent these depredations he fixed up a board, on which he painted or chalked the following lines:—

> "Pray ye, nebbers, dunnet pull;
> I'll gi' ye a pey-scode when they're full.
> If ye it 'em when they're swash,
> They'll fill yer belly full o' trash."

Muckelt happened once to be at the Punch Bowl in Crosthwaite, in company with Dr. Bell. Jamie's rhyming abilities were pretty well known, and perhaps sometimes a little envied. Be that as it may, the Doctor challenged Jamie to rhyme him for a wager. Jamie, without a moment's study, produced the following stanza:—

> "At your request,

I'll du me best;
But ya' thing I implore—
If Dr. Bell
Can du as well,
To trouble me no more."

The Doctor acknowledged himself outdone, and paid his forfeit.

On another occasion Jamie had staid at the Punch Bowl till he was rather top-heavy, and fell into the fire and burnt himself. The next day he went to the house to discharge his bill, and gave them, in addition to their regular charge, the following verse:—

"Thear is some men, for want o' sense,
Will run ther sels to vast expense;
An' I mesel, for want o' greace,
Fell into t' fire an' burnt me feace."

Meeting with a friend one day, in the shambles at Kendal, he said,

"Come, nebber, let us join,
If thou'll buy t' leg I'll buy t' loin;
If thou'll buy t' head I'll buy t' pluck;
An' we'll hev a quart at t' Dog an' Duck."

Many other instances of this rhyming propensity, through all the country, might be produced, would our limits permit.

THE HART'S-HORN TREE.

A TRADITION OF PENRITH.

FOUR miles from Penrith, near the road to Appleby, and in the district which, to this day, bears the name of Whinfell Forest, there formerly stood a fine oak, which bore the name of Hart's-Horn Tree, a name it acquired from a tradition to this effect. In the time of the first Robert de Clifford, about the year 1333, Edward Baliol, King of Scotland, came into Westmorland, and stayed some time with that Lord, at his castles of Appleby, Brougham, and Pendragon. During his visit they ran a stag by a single greyhound, out of Whinfell Forest to Redkirke in Scotland, and back again to the same place. Being both spent, the stag leaped over the pales, and died there; but the greyhound attempting to leap, fell, and died on the opposite side. As a memorial of this incident, the stag's horns were nailed upon a tree just by; and the dog being named Hercules, this couplet obtained currency amongst the people—

"Hercules kill'd Hart-a-grease,[15]
And Hart-a-grease killed Hercules."

"Then went they down into a laund,
These noble archers three;
Eche of them slew a hart of greece,
The best that they could see."

Song of Adam Bell.

In course of time, it is stated, the horns became grafted, as it were, upon the tree, by reason of its bark growing over their root, and there they remained more than three centuries, till, in the year 1648, one of the branches was broken off by some of the army; and ten years afterwards, the remainder was secretly taken down by some mischievous people in the night. "So, now," says Lady Ann Clifford, in her *Diary*, "there is no part thereof remaining, the tree itself being so decayed, and the bark of it so peeled off, that it cannot last long; whereby we may see time brings to forgetfulness many memorable things in this world, be they ever so carefully preserved—for this tree, with the hart's horn in it, was a thing of much note in these parts."

In another part of the same forest, which, like many other forests in this country, as Skiddaw forest, Inglewood forest, &c., has no trace of what it has been but the name, there stood, a few years ago, three enormous oak trees, known by the name of the "Three Brothers." One of them measured thirteen yards in girth.

THE QUAKERESS BRIDE.

A TALE OF THE MOUNTAINS.

THE moon shone full upon the dial of Saint Paul's, and showed the hour-pointer far advanced towards midnight, as Edward Fletcher paused for a moment to inquire the time, and then pursued his way in deep and silent meditation. At an early age, by the death of both his parents, he had been left to the care of an unmarried uncle, who, after giving him a good education, had placed him in a merchant's office, and had since enabled him to become the principal of a mercantile establishment. He had now been for two years the master of a lucrative and increasing business, and being naturally of a social disposition, he began to court the company of those of his own rank. In this way he had spent the evening, and, having accompanied some of his fair companions to their homes, he was returning to his own lodgings in a distant part of the metropolis. The warm and genial influence of Society had called into action the softer emotions of his heart, freed them from the icy fetters which long and arduous attention to business had thrown over them, and caused them again to burst forth and to roll onward in an unbroken current, bearing his thoughts to that far distant period, when, in the twilight of memory, the forms of past events are dim and indistinctly visible.

And he lingered on the recollection with a melancholy pleasure, for it was the happiest period of his existence. He was then the loved and caressed of parents who were now no more. Those joyous days were passed among the pleasant hills and valleys of Westmorland, and now he was confined among the din and bustle of the city. He remembered one fair girl, who was more than his playmate, with whom "he roamed about the braes," pulling the cowslips or the early violets; or at evening sat under the shadow of a spreading elm, telling her the stories which he had read during the day, and listening to the little hymns which her mother had taught her; but of her he knew nothing—she too, probably, was with the dead.

Then he thought of his school-days, with their mischievous tricks and their active sports, and their hard lessons, and the noble boys who were his comrades. Some of them, the gentlest and the most beloved, were also gone to their rest; and the hardy, the active, and enterprising, were pursuing their separate courses of adversity or success; many, like himself, were still bachelors, whilst others enjoyed the delights of domestic felicity in the bosoms of their families. This last subject was one on which he had often deeply pondered. Arrived at that time of life, when the enthusiasm of youth has subsided, before the indifference of age has commenced, he had long felt the solitude of his orphan state; he had been convinced that he did not move in the sphere for which Providence had designed him.

He was alone, among strangers; he was exposed to the thousand little discomforts which are inseparable from the lot of him who has no place which he can feel to be a home. He engaged in the duties of life without spirit or energy, more in imitation of the example of others, than from any heartfelt incitement to action. If prosperity smiled on him, he viewed it with indifference, but the frowns of adversity chilled and depressed him. He wished for some one to share with him in the former, and, by participation, to render the latter less irksome, instead of being compelled to feel the whole weight of its gloom on his own mind, and to brood over his misfortunes in cheerless solitude. His observation had convinced him that marriage alone would give full zest to joy, and soften the stings of sorrow; and now, his heart, softened by the society which he had just left, and by his recollections of former days, nourished and gradually matured the conviction, till at length he firmly resolved to abjure the state, to him miscalled, of "single-blessedness."

By this time he had reached his own door. He had passed through one moon-lit street after another, occupied with his own reflections, unheeding alike the artless laugh of voice, the shout of the drunken reveller, and the noise and tumult of the thronging crowd which poured from one of the theatres.

"Yes," said he, "I'll marry." The rapper was in his hand, and it fell with a heavy knock, as if sounding an "Amen" to his recently-formed resolution.

He retired to his couch, but not to repose. His thoughts continued to oppress and agitate him, and he tossed about restless and sleepless. The hour of midnight, tolled from the neighbouring belfry, had been succeeded by "the wee short hours ayont the twal," gradually lengthening and announcing the dawn of day, before he fell into a short and broken slumber. When he arose he sought his counting-house, but the time passed slowly and heavily on. He spent the day in a state of abstraction, relieved only by a conviction that it was his duty to exert himself more than ever. He would relapse for a while into indolence, and then, suddenly rousing from his stupor, recommence his employment with renewed but short-lived energy; and he rejoiced when the approach of evening allowed him to escape, and to accept the invitation of his friend, Charles Manson, to walk with him in the Regent's Park.

Charles, who was some years his junior, and was studying for the medical profession, was a youth of sanguine temperament—one of those who love to view things on their bright side; who sincerely enjoy the delights of life; and who, if they are visited by affliction, feel it deeply for a time, but soon forget it. He was in high spirits. The fineness of the weather, the number and gay appearance of the company in the Park, and his relaxation from the labours of the day, all tended to enliven him, and animated his converse. Scarcely an equipage rolled by, or a horseman passed them, without furnishing him with occasion for an approving or satirical remark. Edward, however, seemed not to heed his observations, or, if he noticed them at all, it was by a cold nod, or a single syllable of assent.

He passed in silence the various natural and architectural beauties of the place, on which he was accustomed to dilate. The fine Doric portico, and massive grandeur of the Colosseum, the splendid facade of Cumberland Place, the innumerable curiosities of the Zoological Gardens, and the rural loveliness of the wooded lake, were alike unheeded.

At length Charles stopped, and, looking his companion attentively in the face, said to him, "Edward, thou art in love."

"In love," he replied, with a feeble laugh, "not I indeed, what can have given thee such an idea?"

"Thy remarkably grave deportment, moping abstraction, and disregard for all that's worth seeing. Thou hast passed unnoticed many of thy favourite subjects of remark; thou hast allowed the most magnificent carriages, and some of our greatest public characters, to pass thee unobserved, coldly assenting to my words, or 'nodding thy head like a mandarin in a tea-shop'—I am persuaded that thou art in love."

"Well, Charles, I own that, though not yet in love, I trust I soon shall be, and that my love will be consummated by lasting union. I have long compared the delights of marriage with the discomforts of the bachelor, and last night, bringing my notions to a point, I came to the resolution to marry."

"Make no such rash resolve," said Charles, "but consider the inconveniences as well as the comforts of matrimony. For my own part, having given myself up to the pursuit of study, I am satisfied that a wife would retard my progress. It would be impossible for me to pay that undivided attention to my profession, which my duty, not more than my inclination demands. Few eminent men have been married. The rule which prevents Roman Catholic clergymen from being so, was doubtless the result of great experience and deep conviction on the part of its framers, that it tended to draw the thoughts from the functions of the sacerdotal office. So study and celibacy for me; or if I be married, let my library be my bride."

"And a wife and happiness for me!" replied Edward. "What benefit is there in amassing a large store of knowledge, which may never be required, and at the same time neglecting the enjoyment of female society, and despising its aid as the minister of virtue. The reasons which induce thee to continue single do not affect me, and, in fact, I should rather seek a wife to incite me to great exertion, than merely continue in the spiritless pursuit of wealth or knowledge."

"And what," asked Charles, "are the requisite qualities of such a wife?"

"She must," said Edward, "be a woman whose virtues are the fruit of religious conviction; she must be modest without affectation, and cheerful without boldness; lovely in person, and accomplished in mind."

"Let me try to guess who she is," said Charles; and he named some of their female acquaintance who, he thought, best answered the description.

But no! Edward's ideas of female excellence were so refined, that none of these came up to the standard. Each had some fault which might have passed unobserved by others, but could not escape the discriminating eye of our philosophic bachelor.

Lucy was "a blue stocking." She spent her time in the study of foreign languages and abstruse sciences; and her mind, occupied in such recondite pursuits, could not be expected to bend to the homely and unpretending duties of a household.

Elizabeth was "a butterfly:"—a giddy, thoughtless child of nature, content with the powers which nature had bestowed, and regardless of cultivating and improving them; enjoying the present, as though it comprised the whole period of her existence, and as if there would be no future which called for preparation. An imprudent woman was unsuitable for a wife.

Emma was "an egotist." All her regard seemed to be spent upon her own person. She was constantly admiring herself in the mirror, arranging some irregularity in the fold of her kerchief, or some unevenness in her sleeves, or trying some new posture to show her form to advantage: and she who was filled with self-love would care little for the happiness of her husband.

Mary ran into the opposite extreme. He admired simplicity, but he disliked negligence. Some part of her dress was often in disorder; a string was wanting in her cap, or a lock of hair hung loosely over her forehead; and neatness was an indispensable requisite for the partner of his life.

Jane was "a chatter-box;" gay and volatile, her tongue ran on in ceaseless prattle, without giving utterance to one idea, the result either of observation or reflection. Her words sounded prettily enough to the ear, but they left no impression on the mind; and thought and foresight ought to belong to every one who might become the head of a family.

Judith was "a mere negation." She was, perhaps, blameless in regard to the actual commission of offence, but she was supine and indolent in virtuous exertion. If she did no evil, she did little good. The course of her life was one dead level, without rise and without depression. She acted so as to save appearances with the world; but her heart was a stranger to every generous impulse, her hand was seldom stretched out in active benevolence, and her mind was ignorant of the practical operation of religion and piety. He looked to marriage for a stimulus to renewed exertion, but he could expect no aid from one so listless and apathetic.

"Most exact of men!" exclaimed Charles, "thy conduct is a perfect anomaly. Attempting to reason on the most illogical of all passions—laying down a proposition that thou wilt marry, before falling in love, and finding fault with those of the fair sex, who are admired and followed, even by those who never wish to be lovers. Throw off this fastidiousness; or, depend upon it, that it will be long before thou art a husband, and before I am left alone in the ranks of celibacy."

They parted—but the feeling daily increased and became stronger in the mind of Edward. He sought society more eagerly than ever; but though he felt a transient gratification in its variety, he found, in the retrospect, nothing but disappointment. He met with none on whom he could centre his affections. Each had some fault which rendered her unfit for a wife. He met with many whom he admired, many whom he could respect as friends, but none whom he could love with that fervour and singleness of heart which he considered due to her whom he should make his own. And yet he saw his companions select their partners, and live apparently in married felicity. Even the fair ones whom he had so severely criticised and censured, were respectively united to admiring and joyous husbands. Yet in vain did he seek for some pure, spotless being, who might realize his opinion of the feminine character; love seemed to be a tempting fruit hung beyond his reach. He began to doubt whether he was not differently constituted from the generality of his species, and incapable of their susceptibilities; yet when he thought of his early affections to his parents and the fair companion of his youth, and when he referred to the feelings that even now burned in his bosom, he was convinced that he only wanted the opportunity to prove himself possessed of the finest sympathies of humanity.

It was midsummer: the fashionable part of the community had left London for their seats in the country, and Edward, tired of its suffocating heat, its forsaken squares, and desolate streets, resolved also to leave it, and revisit, for the first time since his boyhood, the beautiful scenery of his native Westmorland.

He took the coach to Kendal, and there left it; preferring to proceed on foot, as allowing him greater liberty in choosing his route, and in diverging from the high roads when interest or curiosity might prompt him to wander. For a week he rambled through the most picturesque districts of the country, climbing its hills, while the exercise and the bracing air improved his health; rowing on its lakes, and treading its flowery meads, which spoke of peace and comfort to his mind; or gazing on its waterfalls till his sorrow and disquiet were forgotten in the contemplation. But what were his feelings as he approached the place of his nativity? He stole up the narrow lane that led to it from the main road, and cautiously drew near. He thought that the little croft behind was strangely diminished in size, and that the house had an altered and more homely appearance than he expected; yet over the arch-way were the initials of his parents' names, "R. & S. F., 1795."

He looked through the garden-gate, and at the well-known door sat the mistress of the house, employed with needlework, whilst a young child gambolled along the walks. How often had his mother sat there, occupied in the same manner, and smiled on his infant frolics! He found that his parents were forgotten, and the names of the neighbours were strange to him; even the heavy-clogged hind, of whom he made the inquiry, who was homeward "dragging his weary way," eyed him, as if half-suspicious of some sinister intention. Amid all his distress, he had been accustomed to reflect on that place, and on the early days he had spent there, with feelings of pleasure: when the clouds gathered blackest around him, he remembered them as a gleam of sunshine in his existence, which, overcast as it had been, might yet dispel the shades, and shed its bright glory over the evening of his days. And thus to be awakened to the sad reality, to find himself unknown on the threshold of his father's house, an alien in the place of his birth; to seek in vain for the friends of his youth; to feel that he was alone in the world, and must buffet with it single-handed; to find his last remaining solace depart, and thus to become fully aware of the solitariness of his situation—convinced him alike that he had drawn an overcharged picture of the past, and that doubt and uncertainty appertained to the future—

"He turned and left the spot;
Ah, do not deem him weak,
For dauntless was that youthful heart,
Though a tear was on his cheek."

He pursued his journey; and, on the morrow, after a long ramble across the hills, reached a small and secluded village, where he thought to remain for a day or two. After he had dined, he went out to enjoy the fine views which its vicinity afforded. The road lay along the side of a hill which, on the one hand, was covered with heather, interspersed with large stones, whose grey and wrinkled fronts looked out from the purple blossoms dancing in the breeze, like age surveying the pastimes of youth; and, on the other, was bordered by trees, whose light waving branches gave an occasional glimpse of the lake beyond them. A small avenue opening it to the view, and offering a smooth bank for his seat, he lay down to repose. The green boughs overhead shaded him from the rays of the sun; before him, in the distance, were some of Westmorland's loftiest hills, standing boldly out in the clear blue sky, heathery-clad at their tops, but, at their base, yellow with waving corn, green with luxuriant pastures, or dark with extensive woods; whence rose the smoke of the peasant's cot, the spire of a village church, or the bold front of some magnificent mansion; while, immediately before him, the lake spread its expanse of beauty, its waters calm as a mirror, or curled by the breeze into mimic and noiseless wavelets. A boat moved slowly from behind one of the islands, rowed by one whose dress showed him to be no professed sailor, and in the pause between the grating of the oars on its side, and their splashing in the water, the sound of a soft voice came in song from a lady sitting at the stern. This "touched the string on which hung all his sorrows."

"And is there not," said he—"is there not some being like that for me; is there none on earth to whom I may speak of love? Am I, alone, of all my race doomed to drag on a long and weary life, a solitary, friendless creature? I have formed my notions of excellence at an elevation to which human nature does not attain; I will banish these vain ideas; lower my scale of excellence, as to the external and less important parts of personal character, and return into the world, determined to be pleased, to imitate the example of my fellowmen, and, like them, to be happy."

He was roused by a voice near him, and, on turning, he perceived a mendicant asking alms of a young plainly-dressed lady. He arose from his recumbent posture, and, for the first time, attracted her attention. She gave but one enquiring glance, blushed deeply, slipped the money hurriedly into the extended palm, and went on her way, followed by the benedictions of the grateful sufferer.

By that mysterious principle, that sort of mental magnetism, existing in every bosom, by which we are instantly and unaccountably attracted to one whom we have never seen before, but whom we feel an irresistible desire often to meet—a feeling which time or distance may perhaps diminish, but which nothing but death can extinguish—Edward felt, as he returned to his inn, determined, if it were possible, to have an interview with the fair stranger. Often did she pass before him in the visions of the night; often was his sleep broken by his dreams, but they were dreams of happiness and joy.

The Sabbath morn called him to seek the meeting-house of his sect, which was situate at a short distance from the village. There it stood, with its gray walls and flagged roof—its bright small-paned windows, and weather-beaten door and shutters; its shade of arching lime-trees, and its green grave-yard, surrounded by a low wall and an humble wicket, on which the peasant might lean and moralise; for the dread of desecration which encircles the burial places in cities with palisadoes and chevaux-de-frise had not reached the inhabitants of that peaceful land. Its interior corresponded with the neatness and simplicity of its outward appearances. The walls seemed to have been recently white-washed, and the sand on the floor cracked beneath his tread, as he sought a seat on one of the old oaken forms.

Few were the assembled worshippers. An aged man, dressed in the good old-fashioned drab coat, and three-decked hat, from beneath which hung a few locks of reverend gray, sat under the gallery, resting upon his staff; beneath him was a stout, hale man, of the middle age, whose features bespoke him to be his son, and whose wife was sitting on the adjoining form. The seat parallel to that on which Edward sat, contained some young women, whose features he could not discern; and several, whose dress showed them to be servants, or not connected with the body, were scattered about on the back benches. But though small was the assembly, and humble the place of gathering, whether it arose from the quiet that reigned around, the effect of the past week's journey, or the events connected with it, never did Edward feel more of the pure spirit of devotion, never did he retire from a house of worship more strengthened and refreshed in spirit.

At the close of the meeting, the old friend kindly shook him by the hand, and invited him to his house. Pleased with his venerable appearance, and wishing to become further acquainted with him, Edward accepted the invitation.

"Come," said the ancient, "thou's stronger nor me, let me lean on thy airm;" and, thus supported on the one hand, and with his stick in the other, they walked at a slow pace through two or three fields, and then found themselves at his door. His house was of brick, overgrown in the front with large pear-trees, whose dark foliage strongly contrasted with the clean white windows. A small plot before it, defended by a green paling, was filled with pinks, roses, campanulas, and other summer flowers; at the one end a large, well-stocked orchard extended down the hill-side beyond which, in the distance, were seen the blue waters of the lake; and, at the other, was the farm-yard, with its various out-buildings, its herds of lowing cattle, and troops of poultry. The old man introduced his son, who had arrived before them, by the name of James Summers, and then turning to Edward, said, "but as I don't knaw tha name, I can only half perform my duty."

"My name," he said "is Edward Fletcher."

"From thy dialect," said the son, "I suppose thou art from London."

"Yes, I live there at present, but I was born at Rockgill, about twelve miles to the west of this place."

"What!" inquired the son, "was thy father's name Richard Fletcher?"

"It was," Edward replied, "but he has been long dead."

"I know he has; he was an intimate friend of ours; in fact we were his next neighbours, till the advanced age and increasing infirmities of my father, rendered it necessary for me to assist in the management of his farm. I am heartily glad to see thee; thou must protract thy stay with us, for we have been too long separated to part soon."

"Ay," added his wife, "many a time have I dandled thee on my knee when a child, and Eliza and thou used to wander about together from morning till night."

"What's getten them?" asked the old man, "they are langer nor common in comin' in."

As he spoke the door opened, and the sisters entered the room.

"Why," said the old man, "ye ran off to-day, and didn't come an' help me hame as ye used to do!"

"O! grandfather," said Eliza, "we saw thou wast too well assisted to need our aid."

"Ay, and wha think ye my helper was?—naebody else but Edward Fletcher, that used to play wi' thee when ye were bairns, and that thou sae often talks aboot."

Edward observed her blush deeply at this remark. He had at once recognized her as the lady who had yesterday crossed his path, and as he now accosted her, he felt all his prepossessions in her favour incalculably increased. Her personal appearance was very pleasing. She was rather tall. Her form was slender and graceful, and her complexion exceedingly fair. Her chestnut hair was parted on her forehead, a few stray tresses escaped from the border of her cap, and her light blue eyes sparkled with innocent cheerfulness and unobtrusive benevolence. Her sister, a few years younger, was also a lovely girl, but her form and features were less fully developed.

Placed on this footing, Edward soon felt himself at home, and was delighted with the family into whose society he had fallen; but his observation was chiefly directed to the elder daughter. The more he saw, and the more he conversed with her, the more strongly did she rivet his affections. He found her possessed of a naturally strong, and highly-cultivated mind, stored with knowledge of the most useful kind; with a sweet and gentle disposition, and with a heart in which religion and virtue held supreme place. As he conversed with her, and found that her language breathed of an intellectual and religious spirit, he thought that in her were gathered all the qualities which he had so long sought for in vain. But it was not till the cool of the day, when they walked together by the lake, that he became fully aware of the change which the events of the last twenty-four hours had wrought upon him.

He was with her, whose mere glance had spoken to his inmost heart; her who was the playmate of his infancy—the only human being, except his parents, to whom he had ever looked with a higher feeling than that of esteem: he found that his first impression was increased by future acquaintance; that her features feebly shadowed forth her mental excellence, her modesty, good sense, and religious feeling;—he was with her in his native land at the close of that day, when, if the mind may be allowed to dwell upon any earthly feeling, it is upon that of honourable youthful love, the most purified of mortal passions. They talked of the joys of former days, of the many little incidents which formed the chain of remembrance of their past pleasure, of the mutual thoughts of each other which had lingered in their bosoms; and before the expiration of Edward's sojourn the foundation was laid of a connection which might only terminate with life.

He returned to the metropolis an altered man. His gloom and abstraction had vanished, and he pursued his vocation with redoubled assiduity. But still his heart was absent in "the north countrie," and many a journey did he take thither, no longer to admire the beauty of its scenery, but to indulge himself with the company of her, whose lot in after life was to be bound up with his own. She accepted the offer of his hand; the consent of her parents was asked and received, the requisite formalities gone through, and the necessary arrangements completed, when he asked his friend Charles to accompany him to his marriage. After some demur, on account of the pressing nature of his studies, and the difference of opinion between them as to the propriety of the step, Charles consented to go with him.

When they arrived at the house, they were of course warmly welcomed. The morrow was appointed for the wedding, and, as many relatives had been invited from distant parts, great preparations were making for their accommodation. Eliza seized the opportunity of stealing away, unobserved, once more to visit her chosen walks and favourite seats, and to bid adieu to the scenes where she had spent the blissful days of youth. When she returned, she retired to her room, and having thrown off her bonnet and gloves, she pondered on the circumstances of her present situation. She was about to leave a peaceful home, tender parents, and affectionate friends; but to-morrow she would be a bride: she would gain one who was more to her than all these, who would cherish and protect her; and the tear that trickled adown her cheek, was gilded by the beam of a pure and subdued love. Then, turning her thoughts to Him who made, and had preserved her, she uttered a sincere and fervent prayer for his continued mercy and protection.

Never, perhaps, was the old meeting-house so filled as on the morning of the marriage. Besides the procession of friends and relatives from the house, the neighbours had gathered from far and near to witness the nuptial ceremony of one who was universally respected and beloved: and though there were none of those signs of outward show by which such occasions are commonly distinguished, though there was no firing of cannon, no ringing of bells, no flying of flags, yet it was not less a union of two faithful hearts, nor did their vow of "affection until death" sound less solemnly and impressively on the ears of the hushed assembly.

O not in the halls of the noble and proud,
Where fashion assembles her glittering crowd,
Where all is in beauty and splendour array'd,
Were the nuptials perform'd of the meek Quaker maid.

Nor yet in the temple those rites which she took,
By the altar, the mitre-crown'd bishop, and book:
Where oft in bright jewels doth stand the fair bride,
To whisper those vows which through life shall abide.

The building was humble yet sacred to Him,
Before whom the pomp of religion is dim;
Whose presence is not to the temple confin'd,
But dwells with the contrite and lowly of mind.

'Twas there, all unveil'd, save by modesty stood
The Quakeress Bride, in her pure satin hood,
Her charms unadorn'd by the garland or gem,

Yet fair as the lily just plucked from the stem.

A tear glisten'd bright in her dark shaded eye,
And her bosom half utter'd a tremulous sigh,
As the hand she had pledged was confidingly given,
And the low murmured accents recorded in heaven.

I've been at the bridal where wealth spread the board,
Where the sparkling red wine in rich goblets was pour'd:
Where the priest in his surplice from ritual read,
And the solemn response was impressively said.

I've seen the fond sire, in his thin locks of gray,
Give the pride of his heart to the bridegroom away;
While he brush'd the big tear from his deep-furrowed cheek,
And bow'd the assent which his lips might not speak.

But in all the array of the costlier scene,
Nought seem'd in my eye so sincere in its mien;
No language so fully the heart to resign,
As the Quakeress Bride's, "Until death I am thine!"

Edward found in wedlock all the happiness of which he was in quest; nay, in his relation of a husband and a parent, he partook of many a heartfelt joy, and many a dear and tender feeling, which, in his days of speculative bachelorhood, he was not able to anticipate. No longer a dweller among strangers, living in the cold and cheerless atmosphere of a hired lodging, and meeting only from the other inmates of the house with that common-place regard which exists between those who have little community of feeling, he was happy in the delights of his home, in the smiles of his child, in the warm affection of his loved and lovely wife. He no longer sought the company of others as a relief from his cares; he found an enchaining attraction to his own fireside. No longer neglectful, or indifferent to the result of his mercantile engagements, he entered upon them with increased ardour, not with the base and grovelling view of amassing unprofitable wealth, but as an honourable employment, affording him the means of supporting those who are dependent upon him, and of relieving the distresses of his fellow-creatures.

In difficulty, his wife was a constant, judicious adviser. She endeavoured to mitigate his afflictions, she attended him with unremitting care in sickness, she heightened his joys, and alleviated his sorrows. Her intellectual endowments qualified her to be his companion in study, and she trod with him the humbler walks of literature and science. Her mild and amiable disposition softened every harsh and unkind feeling of his heart, while her piety assisted him in endeavouring to perform those high and holy duties which man owes to his Maker. No longer ill at ease with himself or the world, he became a useful member of the great human family, desirous of fulfilling his allotted part, by engaging actively in schemes of philanthropy, and in the exercise of a pure, unostentatious benevolence.

So apparent, indeed, was his happiness, that it was soon rumoured even of Charles Manson, that, having become a convert to his opinions, and being convinced that domestic life is the surest source of present happiness, and a genial nursery of those qualities which fit us for future felicity, had taken more than one trip among the green hills of Westmorland, in quest of a companion for life.

My tale is simple, but so are truth, and virtue, and happiness; and to enforce this moral is the purpose of my story. I might have filled my canvas with the brilliant colours and iris tints of romance and fiction; but the eye of the spectator would have been dazzled, and he would have found nothing on which to rest his gaze: the chaste and sober hues of truth alone are healthful to the mental sight. If in this humble colouring I have so traced the picture of Edward and Eliza, as to show that marriage is one of the first of blessings, and that its joys, though removed from the superficial and fastidious, may yet be attained by the simple and sincere; if I have at all shown what are the qualities to be sought for in a virtuous wife, and how, and where they may be found; if thus my humble page shall have shed a beam of hope over the desponding and the solitary, its object will be attained.

> "Domestic happiness! thou only bliss
> Of paradise, that has survived the fall!
> Though few now taste thee unimpaired and pure,
> Or tasting, long enjoy thee; too infirm,
> Or too incautious, to preserve thy sweets
> Unmixed with drops of bitter, which neglect
> Or temper sheds into thy crystal cup;
> Thou art the nurse of virtue; in thine arms
> She smiles appearing as in truth she is,
> Heaven-born, and destined to the skies again.
> Thou art not known where pleasure is adored,
> That reeling goddess with the zoneless waist.
> And wandering eyes, still leaning on the arm
> Of novelty, her fickle, frail support.
> For thou art meek and constant, hating change,
> And finding, in the calm of truth-tried love,
> Joys that her stormy raptures never yield."

THE BEAUTY OF BUTTERMERE;

OR, TRAGEDY IN REAL LIFE.

JOHN HATFIELD, who acquired the appellation of the Keswick Impostor, and whose extraordinary villany excited universal hatred, was born in 1759, at Mortram, in Cheshire, of low parentage, but possessing great natural abilities. His face was handsome, his person genteel, his eyes blue, and his complexion fair.

After some domestic depredations—for in his early days he betrayed an iniquitous disposition—he quitted his family, and was employed as traveller to a linen-draper in the north of England. In the course of this service, he became acquainted with a young woman, who was nursed, and resided at a farmer's house in the neighbourhood of his employer. She had been, in her earlier life, taught to consider the people with whom she lived as her parents. Remote from the gaieties and follies of polished life, she was unacquainted with the allurements of fashion, and considered her domestic duties as the only object of her consideration. When this deserving girl had arrived at a certain age, the honest farmer explained to her the secret of her birth; he told her, that, notwithstanding she had always considered him as her parent, he was, in fact, only her poor guardian; and that she was the natural daughter of Lord Robert Manners, who intended to give her £1000, provided she married with his approbation.

This discovery soon reached the ears of Hatfield; he immediately paid his respects at the farmer's, and having represented himself as a young man of considerable expectations in the wholesale linen business, his visits were not discountenanced. The farmer, however, thought it incumbent on him to acquaint his lordship with a proposal made to him by Hatfield, that he would marry the young woman, if her relations were satisfied with their union, but on no other terms. This had so much the appearance of an honourable and prudent intention, that his lordship, on being made acquainted with the circumstances, desired to see the lover. He accordingly paid his respects to the noble and unsuspecting parent, who, conceiving the young man to be what he represented himself, gave his consent at the first interview; and, the day after the marriage took place, presented the bridegroom with a draft on his banker for £1,500. This took place about 1771 or 1772.

Shortly after the receipt of his lordship's bounty, Hatfield set off for London; hired a small phæton; was perpetually at the coffee-houses in Covent Garden; described himself to whatever company he chanced to meet, as a near relation of the Rutland family; vaunted of his parks and hounds; but as great liars have seldom good memories, he so varied in his descriptive figures, that he acquired the appellation of *Lying Hatfield*.

The marriage portion now exhausted, he retreated from London, and was scarcely heard of for about ten years, when he again visited the metropolis, having left his wife, with three daughters, to depend on the precarious charity of her relations. Happily she did not long survive; and the author of her calamities, during his stay in London, soon experienced calamity himself, having been arrested, and committed to King's Bench prison, for a debt amounting to the sum of £160. Several unfortunate gentlemen, then confined in the same place, had been of his parties when he flourished in Covent Garden, and perceiving him in great poverty, frequently invited him to dinner; yet such was his unaccountable disposition, that notwithstanding he knew there were people present who were thoroughly acquainted with his character, still he would continue to describe his Yorkshire park, his estate in Rutlandshire, settled upon his wife, and generally wind up the whole with observing how vexatious it was to be confined at the suit of a paltry tradesman for so insignificant a sum, at the very moment when he had thirty men employed in cutting a piece of water near the family mansion in Yorkshire.

At the time Hatfield became a prisoner in the King's Bench, the unfortunate Valentine Morris, formerly governor of St. Vincent's, was confined in the same place. This gentleman was frequently visited by a clergyman of the most benevolent and humane disposition. Hatfield soon directed his attention to this good man, and one day earnestly invited to attend him to his chamber; after some preliminary apologies, he implored the worthy pastor never to disclose what he was going to communicate. The divine assured him the whole should remain in his bosom. "Then," said Hatfield, "you see before you a man nearly allied to the house of Rutland, and possessed of estates (here followed the old story of the Yorkshire park, the Rutlandshire property, &c., &c.,); yet notwithstanding all this wealth, continued he, I am detained in this wretched place for the insignificant sum of £160. But the truth is, Sir, I would not have my situation known to any man in the world but my worthy relative, his Grace of Rutland. Indeed, I would rather remain a captive for ever. If you would have the goodness to pay your respects to this worthy nobleman, and frankly describe how matters are, he will at once send me the money by you; and this mighty business will not only be instantly settled, but I shall have the satisfaction of introducing you to a connection which may be attended with happy consequences."

The honest clergyman readily undertook the commission; paid his respects to the Duke, and pathetically described the unfortunate situation of his amiable relative. His Grace of Rutland, not recollecting at the moment such a name as Hatfield, expressed his astonishment at the application. This reduced the worthy divine to a very awkward situation, and he faltered in his speech, when he began making an apology; which the Duke perceiving, he very kindly observed, that he believed the whole was some idle tale of an impostor, for that he never knew any person of the name mentioned, although he had some faint recollection of hearing Lord Robert Manners, his relation, say that he had married a natural daughter of his to a tradesman in the north of England, and whose name he believed was Hatfield.

The Reverend was so confounded that he immediately retired and proceeded to the prison, where he gave the impostor, in the presence of Mr. Morris, a most severe lecture. But the appearance of this venerable man, as his friend, had the effect which Hatfield expected; for the Duke sent to inquire if he was the man that married the natural daughter of Lord Robert Manners, and, being satisfied as to the fact, despatched a messenger with £200, and had him released.

In 1784, his Grace of Rutland was appointed Lord Lieutenant of Ireland; and shortly after his arrival in Dublin, Hatfield made his appearance in that city. He immediately, on his landing, engaged a suite of rooms at a hotel in College Green, and represented himself as nearly allied to the Viceroy, but that he could not appear at the castle until his horses, servants, and carriages were arrived, which he ordered, before leaving England, to be shipped at Liverpool. The easy and familiar manner in which he addressed the master of the hotel, perfectly satisfied him that he had a man of consequence in his house, and matters were arranged accordingly. This being adjusted, Hatfield soon found his way to Lucas's coffee-house, a place which people of a certain rank generally frequent; and, it being a new scene, the Yorkshire park, the Rutlandshire estate, and the connection with the Rutland family, stood their ground very well for about a month.

At the expiration of this time, the bill at the hotel amounted to £60 and upwards. The landlord became importunate, and after expressing his astonishment at the non-arrival of Mr. Hatfield's domestics, etc., requested he might be permitted to send in his bill. This did not in the least confuse Hatfield; he immediately told the master of the hotel, that very unfortunately his agent, who received the rents of his estates in the north of England, was then in Ireland, and held a public employment; he lamented that his agent was not then in Dublin, but he had the pleasure to know his stay in the country would not exceed three days. This satisfied the landlord; and at the expiration of the three days, he called upon the gentleman whose name Hatfield had given him, and presented the account. Here followed another scene of confusion and surprise. The supposed agent of the Yorkshire estate very frankly told the man who delivered the bill, that he had no other knowledge of the person who sent him than what common report furnished him with, that his general character in London was that of a romantic simpleton whose plausibilities had imposed on several people, and plunged himself into repeated difficulties.

The landlord retired, highly thankful for the information, and immediately arrested his guest who was lodged in the prison of the Marshalsea. Hatfield had scarcely seated himself in his new lodgings, when he visited the jailor's wife in her apartment, and in a whisper, requested of her not to tell any person that she had in her custody a near relation of the then Viceroy. The woman, astonished at the discovery, immediately showed him into the best apartment in the prison, had a table provided, and she, her husband, and Hatfield, constantly dined together, for nearly three weeks, in the utmost harmony and good humour.

During this time he had petitioned the Duke for another supply, who, apprehensive that the fellow might continue his impositions in Dublin, released him, on condition of his immediately quitting Ireland; and his grace sent a servant, who conducted him on board the packet that sailed the next tide for Holyhead.

In 1792, he came to Scarbro', introduced himself to the acquaintance of several persons of distinction in that neighbourhood, and insinuated that he was, by the interest of the Duke of Rutland, soon to be one of the representatives in parliament for the town of Scarbro'. After several weeks' stay at the principal inn, his imposture was detected by his inability to pay the bill. Soon after his arrival in London, he was arrested for this debt, and thrown into prison. He had been eight years and a half in confinement, when a Miss Nation, of Devonshire, to whom he had become known, paid his debts, took him from prison, and gave him her hand in marriage.

Soon after he was liberated, he had the good fortune to prevail with some highly respectable merchants in Devonshire to take him into partnership with them; and, with a clergyman to accept his drafts to a large amount. He made upon this foundation a splendid appearance in London; and, before the general election, even proceeded to canvass the rotten burgh of Queenborough. Suspicions in the meantime arose, in regard to his character, and the state of his fortune. He retired from the indignation of his creditors, and was declared a bankrupt, in order to bring his villanies to light. Thus, having left behind his second wife and two infant children at Tiverton, he visited other places; and, at length, in July, 1802, arrived at the Queen's Head in Keswick, in a handsome travelling carriage, but without any servant, where he assumed the name of the Hon. Alexander Augustus Hope, brother of the Earl of Hopetoun, M.P., for Linlithgow.

From Keswick, as his head-quarters, he made excursions in every direction amongst the neighbouring valleys; meeting, generally, a good deal of respect and attention, partly on account of his handsome equipage, and still more from his visiting cards, which designated him as "the Honourable Alexander Augustus Hope." Some persons had discernment enough to doubt of this; for his breeding and deportment, though showy, had a tinge of vulgarity about it; he was grossly ungrammatical in his ordinary conversation. He received letters under this assumed name—which might be through collusion with accomplices—but he himself continually franked letters by that name. That being a capital offence, not only a forgery, but (as a forgery on the post-office) sure to be prosecuted, nobody presumed to question his pretensions any longer; and henceforward, he went to all places with the consideration attached to an earl's brother. All doors flew open at his approach; boats, boatmen, nets, and the most unlimited sporting privileges, were placed at the disposal of the "Honourable" gentleman; and the hospitality of the whole country taxed itself to offer a suitable reception to the patrician Scotchman.

Nine miles from Keswick, by the nearest route, lies the lake of Buttermere. Its margin, which is overhung by some of the loftiest and steepest of Cumbrian mountains, exhibits on either side few traces of human neighbourhood; the level area, where the hills recede enough to allow of any, is of a wild, pastoral character, or almost savage; the waters of the lake are deep and sullen; and the barrier mountains, by excluding the sun for much of its daily course, strengthen the gloomy impressions. At the foot of this lake (that is, at the end where its waters issue), lie a few unornamented fields, through which rolls a little brook-like river, connecting it with the larger lake of Crummock; and at the edge of this little domain, upon the roadside, stands a cluster of cottages, so small and few, that, in the richer tracts of the islands, they would scarcely be complimented with the name of hamlet. One of these, the principal, belonged to an independent proprietor, called, in the local dialect, a "Statesman;" and more, perhaps, for the sake of gathering any little local news, than with much view to pecuniary profit at that era, this cottage offered the accommodations of an inn to traveller and his horse.

Rare, however, must have been the mounted traveller in those days, unless visiting Buttermere for itself, for the road led to no further habitations of man, with the exception of some four or five pastoral cabins, equally humble, in Gatesgarth dale. Hither, however, in an evil hour for the peace of this little brotherhood of shepherds, came the cruel spoiler from Keswick, and directed his steps to the once happy cottage of poor Mary, the daughter of Mr. and Mrs. Robinson, an old couple, who kept the inn, and had, by their industry, gained a little property. She was the only daughter, and probably her name had never been known to the public, but for the account given of her by the author of *A Fortnight's Ramble to the Lakes in Westmorland, Lancashire, and Cumberland.* His errand was to witness or share in char-fishing; for in Derwentwater (the lake of Keswick) no char is found, which breeds only in the deeper waters, such as Windermere, Crummock, Buttermere, &c.

Hatfield now became acquainted with an Irish gentleman, an M.P., who had been resident with his family some months at Keswick. With this gentleman, and under his immediate protection, there was likewise a young lady of family and fortune, and of great personal attractions. One of the means which Hatfield used to introduce himself to this respectable family was the following:—Understanding that the gentleman had been a military man, he took an army list from his pocket, and pointed to his assumed name, the Honourable Alexander Augustus Hope, lieutenant-colonel of the 14th regiment of foot. This new acquaintance daily gained strength; and he shortly paid his addresses to the daughter of the above gentleman, and obtained her consent. The wedding clothes were bought; but previously to the wedding-day being fixed, she insisted that the pretended Colonel Hope should introduce the subject formally to her friends. He now pretended to write letters; and, while waiting for the answers, proposed to employ that time in a trip to Lord Hopetoun's seat, &c.

From this time he played a double game; his visits to Keswick became frequent, and his suit to the young lady assiduous and fervent. Still, however, both at Keswick and Buttermere, he was somewhat shy of appearing in public. He was sure to be engaged in a fishing expedition on the day on which any company was expected at the public house at Buttermere; and he never attended the church at Keswick but once.

Finding his schemes baffled to obtain this young lady and her fortune, he now applied himself wholly to gain possession of Mary Robinson, who was a fine young woman of eighteen, and acted as waiter. In a situation so solitary, the stranger had unlimited facilities for enjoying her company, and recommending himself to her favour. Among the neighbours he made the most minute inquiries into every circumstance relating to her and her family. Doubts about his pretensions never arose in so simple a place as this; they were over-ruled before they could well have arisen, by the opinion now general in Keswick, that he really was what he pretended to be; and thus, with little demur, except in the shape of a few natural words of parting anger from a defeated or rejected rustic admirer, the young woman gave her hand in marriage to the showy and unprincipled stranger. He procured a licence, and they were married in the church of Lorton, on the 2nd of October, 1802. A romantic account of the circumstance found its way almost immediately into the newspapers. It thus fell under the notice of various individuals in Scotland, who knew that Colonel Hope, who was said to have married the flower of Buttermere, had been abroad the whole summer, and was now residing in Vienna. Mr. Charles Hope, then Lord Justice Clerk, afterwards President of the Court of Session (a son-in-law of the Earl of Hopetoun), made the fact known, and prompted inquiries which led to the detection of the imposture.

On the day previous to his marriage, Hatfield wrote to Mr. Mansfield, informing him, that he was under the necessity of being absent for ten days on a journey into Scotland, and sent him a draft for thirty pounds, drawn on Mr. Crumpt, of Liverpool, desired him to cash it, and pay some small debts in Keswick with it, and send him over the balance, as he feared he might be short of cash on the road. This Mr. Mansfield immediately did, and sent him ten guineas in addition to the balance. On the Saturday, Wood, the landlord of the Queen's Head, returned from Lorton with the public intelligence, that Colonel Hope had married the Beauty of Buttermere. As it was clear, whoever he was, that he had acted unworthily and dishonourably, Mr. Mansfield's suspicions were of course awakened. He instantly remitted the draft to Mr. Crumpt, who immediately accepted it. Mr. Mansfield wrote to the Earl of Hopetoun. Before the answer arrived, the pretended honourable returned with his wife to Buttermere. He went only as far as Longtown, when he received two letters, seemed much troubled that some friends whom he had expected had not arrived there, stayed three days, and then told his wife that he would again go back to Buttermere.

From this she was seized with fears and suspicions. They returned, however, and their return was made known at Keswick. The late Mr. Harding, the barrister, and a Welsh judge, passing through Keswick, heard of this impostor, and sent his servant over to Buttermere with a note to the supposed Colonel Hope, who observed, "that it was a mistake, and that it was for a brother of his." However, he sent for four horses, and came over to Keswick; drew another draft on Mr. Crumpt for twenty pounds, which the landlord at the Queen's Head had the courage to cash. Of this sum he immediately sent the ten guineas to Mr. Mansfield, who came and introduced him to the judge, as his old friend Colonel Hope. But he made a blank denial that he had ever assumed the name. He had said his name was Hope, but not that he was the honourable member for Linlithgow, &c., &c.; and one who had been his frequent intimate at Buttermere gave evidence to the same purpose.

In spite, however, of his impudent assertions, and those of his associate, the evidence against him was decisive. A warrant was given by Sir Frederick Vane on the clear proof of his having forged and received several franks as the member for Linlithgow; and he was committed to the care of a constable, but allowed to fish on the lake. Having, however, found means to escape, he took refuge for a few days on board a sloop off Ravenglass, and then went in the coach to Ulverston, and was afterwards seen at a hotel in Chester. In the meantime the following advertisement, setting forth his person and manners, was in the public prints:—

"Notorious Impostor, Swindler, and Felon!

"John Hatfield, who lately married a young woman, commonly called the Beauty of Buttermere, under an assumed name; height about five feet ten inches, aged about forty-four, full face, bright eyes, thick eyebrows, strong, but light beard, good complexion, with some colour, thick, but not very prominent nose, smiling countenance, fine teeth, a scar on one of his cheeks near his chin, very long thick light hair, and a great deal of it gray, done up in a club; stiff, square-shouldered, full breast and chest, rather corpulent, and strong limbed, but very active; and has rather a spring in his gait, with apparently a little hitch in bringing up one leg; the two middle fingers of his left hand are stiff from an old wound; he has something of the Irish brogue in his speech; fluent and elegant in his language, great command of words, frequently puts his hand to his heart; very fond of compliments, and generally addressing himself to persons most distinguished by rank or situation; attentive in the extreme to females, and likely to insinuate himself where there are young ladies. He was in America during the war; is fond of talking of his wounds and exploits there, and of military subjects, as well as of Hatfield Hall, and his estates in Derbyshire and Cheshire; and of the antiquity of his family, whom he pretends to trace to the Plantagenets. He makes a boast of having often been engaged in duels; he has been a great traveller also, by his own account, and talks of Egypt, Turkey, and Italy; and, in short, has a general knowledge of subjects, which, together with his engaging manners, is well calculated to impose on the credulous. He had art enough to connect himself with some very respectable merchants in Devonshire, as a partner in business, but having swindled them out of large sums, he was made a separate bankrupt in June, 1802. He cloaks his deception under the mask of religion, appears fond of religious conversation, and makes a point of attending divine service and popular preachers."

Besides blighting the prospects of the poor girl, he had nearly ruined her father by running up a debt of eighteen pounds. His dressing-case, a very elegant piece of furniture, was left behind, and on being opened at Keswick by warrant of a magistrate, was found to contain every article that the most luxurious gentleman could desire, but no papers tending to discover his real name. Afterwards, Mary herself, searching more narrowly, discovered that the box had a double bottom, and in the intermediate recess, found a number of letters addressed to him by his wife and children, under the name of Hatfield. The story of the detection immediately became as notorious as the marriage had been.

Though he was personally known in Cheshire to many of the inhabitants, yet this specious hypocrite had so artfully disguised himself, that he quitted the town without any suspicions before the Bow Street officers reached that place in quest of him. He was then traced to Brielth, in Brecknockshire, and was at length apprehended about sixteen miles from Swansea, and committed to Brecon jail. He had a cravat on, with his initials, J. H., which he attempted to account for by calling himself John Henry.

Before the magistrates he declared himself to be Ludor Henry; and in order to prepossess the honest Cambrians in his favour, boasted that he was descended from an ancient family in Wales, for the inhabitants of which country he had ever entertained a sincere regard. He was, however, conveyed up to town by the Bow Street officers, where he was examined on his arrival before the magistrates. The solicitor for his bankruptcy attended to identify his person, and stated, that the commission of bankruptcy was issued against Hatfield in June, 1802; that he attended the last meeting of the commissioners, but the prisoner did not appear, although due notice had been given in the *Gazette*, and he himself had given notice to the prisoner's wife, at Wakefield near Tiverton, Devon. Mr. Parkyn, the solicitor to the Post-office, produced a warrant from Sir Frederick Vane, Bart., a magistrate for the county of Cumberland, against the prisoner, by the name of the Hon. Alexander Augustus Hope, charging him with felony, by pretending to be a member of parliament of the United Kingdom, and franking several letters by the name of A. Hope, to several persons, which were put into the Post-office at Keswick, in Cumberland, in order to evade the duties of postage. Another charge for forgery, and the charge for bigamy, were explained to him, but not entered into, as he was committed for trial for these charges at the next assizes at Carlisle. He conducted himself with the greatest propriety during his journey to town, and on his examination; but said nothing more than answering a few questions put to him by Sir Richard Ford and the solicitors, affecting to consider himself a persecuted individual, and representing, in particular, that, in the alliance with Mary Robinson, he had been rather sinned against than sinning. Mary, on the other hand, who was now announced to be likely to bear a child to her pretended husband, refused to become accessory to his prosecution. The utmost she could be prevailed on to do against Hatfield was to address the following letter to Sir Richard Ford:—

"The man whom I had the misfortune to marry, and who has ruined me and my aged parents, always told me he was the Hon. Colonel Hope, the next brother of the Earl of Hopetoun. Your grateful and unfortunate servant,

MARY ROBINSON."

At the fourth examination of the impostor, on the 27th of December, this letter was read aloud by the clerk, in the open court. To quote from a chronicle of the time:—"The simplicity of this letter, which, though it breathes the soft murmur of complaint, is free from all virulence, excited in the breast of every person present an emotion of pity and respect for the unmerited sorrows of a female, who has in this whole matter manifested a delicacy of sentiment, and nobleness of mind, infinitely beyond her sphere of education. The feelings of Hatfield could not be enviable; yet he exhibited no symptom of contrition; and when remanded for further examination, retired with the most impenetrable composure."

He was then dressed in a black coat and waistcoat, fustian breeches, and boots, and wore his hair tied behind. His appearance was respectable, though quite in dishabille. The Duke of Cumberland, and several other gentlemen, were present at his examination; in the course of which the following letter was produced:—

"BUTTERMERE, *Oct.* 1, 1802.

"DEAR SIR,—I have this day received Mr. Firkman's kind letter from Manchester, promising me the happiness of seeing you both in about ten days, which will indeed give me great pleasure; and you can, too, be of very valuable service to me at this place, particulars of which, when we meet, though I shall probably write to you again in a few days. The chief purpose for which I write this, is to desire you will be so good as to accept a bill for me, dated Buttermere, the 1st of October, at ten days, and I will either give you cash for it here, or remit to you in time, whichever way you please to say. It is drawn in favour of Nathaniel Montgomery More, Esq. Be pleased to present my best respects to your lady; and say, I hope, ere the winter elapses, to pay her my personal respects; for if you will manage so as to pass a little time with me in Scotland, I will promise to make Liverpool in my way to London. With the truest esteem, I am, Dear Sir, yours ever,

A. HOPE."

"KESWICK, *October the 1st, 1802.*
JOHN CRUMPT, Esq., Liverpool.
Free, A. HOPE."

This letter, it was proved, passed free of postage. Another letter was also produced from his wife at Tiverton, and a certificate of his marriage with Mary of Buttermere. His trial came on August 15th, 1803, at the Assizes for Cumberland, before the Honourable Alexander Thompson, Knt. He stood charged upon the three following indictments:—

1. With having assumed the name and title of the Honourable Alexander Augustus Hope, and pretending to be a member of parliament of the United Kingdom of Great Britain and Ireland; and with having, about the month of October last, under such false and fictitious name and character, drawn a draft or bill of exchange, in the name of Alexander Hope, upon John Crumpt, Esq., for the sum of £20, payable to George Wood, of Keswick, Cumberland, innkeeper, or order, at the end of fourteen days from the date of the said draft or bill of exchange.

2. With making, uttering, and publishing as true, a certain false, forged, and counterfeit bill of exchange, with the name of Alexander Augustus Hope thereunto falsely set and subscribed, drawn upon John Crumpt, Esq., dated the 1st of October, 1802, and payable to Nathaniel Montgomery More, or order, ten days after date, for £30 sterling.

3. With having assumed the name of Alexander Hope, and pretending to be a member of parliament of the United Kingdom of Great Britain and Ireland, the brother of the right Hon. Lord Hopetoun, and a colonel in the army; and under such false and fictitious name and character, at various times in the month of October, 1802, having forged and counterfeited the hand-writing of the said Alexander Hope, in the superscription of certain letters or packets, in order to avoid the payment of the duty on postage.

The prisoner pleaded not guilty to the charge.

The three several indictments having been read, Mr. Scarlett opened the case in an address to the jury; and gave an ample detail of the prisoner's guilt.

In support of what he had advanced, he called Mr. Quick, who was clerk in the house at Tiverton, where Hatfield was partner, who swore to his hand-writing. The Rev. Mr. Nicholson swore that when the prisoner was asked his name, he said it was a comfortable one—Hope.

The evidence for the prosecution having closed, the prisoner addressed himself to the jury. He said he felt some degree of satisfaction in being able to have his sufferings terminated, as they must of course be by their verdict. For the space of nine months he had been dragged from prison to prison, and torn from place to place, subject to all the misrepresentations of calumny.

"Whatever will be my fate," said he, "I am content; it is the award of justice, impartially and virtuously administered. But I will solemnly declare that in all my transactions, I never intended to defraud or injure the persons whose names have appeared in the prosecution. This I will maintain to the last of my life."

After the evidence was gone through, his lordship, Sir A. Thompson, summed up the whole of the evidence and commented upon such parts as peculiarly affected the fate of the prisoner. "Nothing," said his lordship, "could be more clearly proved, than that the prisoner did make the bill or bills in question under the assumed name of Alexander Augustus Hope, with an intention to defraud. That the prisoner used the additional name of Augustus was of no consequence in this question. The evidence proved clearly that the prisoner meant to represent himself to be another character; and under that assumed character, he drew the bills in question. If anything should appear in mitigation of the offences with which the prisoner was charged, they must give them a full consideration; and though his character had been long shaded with obloquy, yet they must not let this in the least influence the verdict they were sworn to give."

The jury consulted about ten minutes, and then returned a verdict—Guilty of Forgery.

During the whole of the trial the court was excessively crowded. The prisoner's behaviour was proper and dignified; and he supported his situation from first to last with unshaken fortitude. He employed himself, during the greatest part of his trial, in writing notes on the evidence given, and in conversing with his counsel.

When the verdict of the jury was given, he manifested no relaxation of his accustomed demeanour. After the court adjourned, he retired from the bar, and was ordered to attend the next morning to receive the sentence of the law. The crowd was immense; and he was allowed a post-chaise from the town-hall to the jail.[16]

At eight o'clock the next morning, the court met again, when the prisoner appeared at the bar to receive his sentence. Numbers of people gathered together to witness this painful duty of the law passed upon one whose appearance, manners, and actions, had excited a most uncommon degree of interest. After proceeding in the usual form, the judge addressed the prisoner in the following impressive terms:—

"John Hatfield, after the long and serious investigation of the charges which have been preferred against you, you have been found guilty by a jury ofyour country.

"You have been distinguished for crimes of such magnitude, as have seldom, if ever, received any mitigation of capital punishment; and in your case, it is impossible it can be limited. Assuming the person, name, and character, of a worthy and respectable officer of a noble family in this country, you have perpetrated and committed the most enormous crimes. The long imprisonment you have undergone has afforded time for your serious reflection, and an opportunity for your being deeply impressed with a sense of the enormity of your crimes, and the justness of that sentence which must be inflicted upon you; and I wish you to be seriously impressed with the awfulness of your situation. I conjure you to reflect with anxious care and deep concern on your approaching end, concerning which much remains to be done. Lay aside now your delusions and impositions, and employ properly the short space you have to live. I beseech you to employ the remaining part of your time in preparing for eternity, so that you may find mercy at the hour of death, and in the day of judgment. Hear, now, the sentence of the law:—That you be carried from hence to the place from whence you came, and from thence to the place of execution, and there to be hung by the neck till you are dead; and may the Lord have mercy on your soul!"

A notion very generally prevailed that he would not be brought to justice; and the arrival of the mail was daily expected with the greatest impatience. No pardon arriving, Saturday, September 3, 1803, was at last fixed upon for the execution.

The gallows was erected the preceding night, between twelve and three, on an island formed by the river Eden, on the north side of the town, between the two bridges. From the hour when the jury found him guilty, he behaved with the utmost serenity and cheerfulness. He talked upon the topics of the day with the greatest interest or indifference. He could scarcely ever be brought to speak of his own case. He neither blamed the verdict, nor made any confession of his guilt. He said he had no intention to defraud those whose names he forged; but was never heard to say that he was to die unjustly. None of his relations ever visited him during his confinement.

The alarming nature of the crime of forgery, in a commercial country, had taught him, from the beginning, to entertain no hope of mercy. By ten in the morning of September 3, his irons were struck off; he appeared as usual, and no one observed any alteration or increased agitation whatever.

Soon after ten o'clock he sent for the *Carlisle Journal*, and perused it for some time. A little after he had laid aside the paper, two clergymen (Mr. Pattison of Carlisle and Mr. Mark of Burgh-on-Sands), attended and prayed with him for about two hours, and drank coffee with him. After they left him, about twelve, he wrote some letters, and in one he enclosed his penknife; it was addressed to London. About this time he also shaved himself; though intrusted with a razor, he never seems to have meditated an attempt upon his life; but it was generally reported on Friday night that he had poisoned himself, though without foundation. To all who spoke with him, he pretended that what he had to suffer was a matter of little consequence. He preferred talking on indifferent subjects. At three, he dined with the jailer, and ate heartily. Having taken a glass or two of wine, he ordered coffee. He took a cup a few minutes before he set out for the place of execution. The last thing he did was to read a chapter from the 2d Corinthians. He had previously marked out this passage for his lesson before he was to mount the scaffold.

The sheriffs, the bailiffs, and the Carlisle volunteer cavalry, attended at the jail door about half-past three, together with a post-chaise and hearse. He was then ordered into the turnkey's lodge, for the purpose of being pinioned, where he inquired of the jailer, who were going in the chaise with him? He was told the executioner and the jailer. He immediately said, "Pray, where is the executioner? I should wish much to see him." The executioner was sent for. Hatfield asked him how he was, and made him a present of some silver in a paper. During the time of his being pinioned, he stood with resolution, and requested he might not be pinioned tight, as he wished to use his handkerchief on the platform; which was complied with. A prodigious crowd had assembled; this was the market day, and people had come from the distance of many miles out of mere curiosity. Hatfield, when he left the prison, wishedall his fellow-prisoners might be happy; he then took farewell of the clergyman, who attended him to the door of the chaise, and mounted the steps with much steadiness and composure. The jailer and executioner went in along with him. The latter had been brought from Dumfries upon a retaining fee of ten guineas.

It was exactly four o'clock when the procession moved from the jail. Passing through the Scotch gate, in about twelve minutes it arrived at the Sands. Half the yeomanry went before the carriage, and the other half behind. Upon arriving on the ground, they formed a ring round the scaffold. It is said that he wished to have the blinds drawn up, but that such an indulgence was held inconsistent with the interest of public justice. When he came in sight of the tree, he said to the jailer, he imagined that was the tree (pointing at it) that he was to die on. On being told yes, he exclaimed, "O! a happy sight—I see it with pleasure!"

As soon as the carriage-door had been opened by the under-sheriff, he alighted with his two companions. A small-cart, boarded over, had been placed under the gibbet, and a ladder was placed against it, which he instantly ascended. He was dressed in a black jacket, black silk waistcoat, fustian pantaloons, shoes, and white cotton stockings. He was perfectly cool and collected. At the same time, his conduct displayed nothing of levity, of insensibility, or of hardihood. He was more anxious to give proof of resignation than of heroism. His countenance was extremely pale, but his hand never trembled. He immediately untied his neckerchief, and placed a bandage over his eyes. Then he desired the hangman, who was extremely awkward, to be as expert as possible about it, and that he would wave a handkerchief when he was ready. The hangman, not having fixed the rope in its proper place, he put up his hand and turned it himself. He also tied his cap, took his handkerchief from his own neck, and tied it about his head also. Then he requested the jailer would step on the platform and pinion his arms a little harder, saying, that when he had lost his senses he might attempt to lift them to his neck. The rope was completely fixed about five minutes before five o'clock; it was slack, and he merely said, "May the Almighty bless you all." Nor did he falter in the least, when he tied the cap, shifted the rope, and took his handkerchief from his neck.

He several times put on a languid and piteous smile. He at last seemed rather exhausted and faint. Having been near three weeks under sentence of death, he must have suffered much, notwithstanding his external bearing; and a reflection of the misery he had occasioned must have given him many an agonizing throb.

Having taken leave of the jailer and sheriff, he prepared himself for his fate. He was at this time heard to exclaim, "My spirit is strong, though my body is weak."

Great apprehensions were entertained that it would be necessary to tie him up a second time. The noose slipped twice, and he fell down about eighteen inches. His feet at last were almost touching the ground; but his excessive weight, which occasioned this accident, speedily relieved him from pain. He expired in a moment, and without any struggle. The ceremony of his hands being tied behind his back, was satisfied by a piece of white tape passed loosely from one to the other; but he never made the smallest effort to relieve himself. He had calculated so well, that his money lasted exactly to the scaffold. As they were setting out, the hangman was going to search him. He threw him half-a-crown, saying,

"This is all my pockets contain."

He had been in considerable distress before he received a supply from his father. He afterwards lived in great style, frequently making presents to his fellow felons. He was considered in the jail as a kind of emperor; he was allowed to do whatever he pleased, and no one took offence at the air of superiority which he assumed.

He was cut down after he had hung about an hour. On the preceding Wednesday he had applied to one of the clergymen who attended him, to recommend him a tradesman to make his coffin. Mr. Bushby, of Carlisle, took measure of him. He did not appear at all agitated while Mr. Bushby was so employed; but told him that he wished the coffin to be a strong oak one, plain and neat.

"I request, Sir," he added, "that after I am taken down, I may be put into the coffin immediately, with the apparel I may have on, and afterwards closely screwed down, put into the hearse which will be in waiting, carried to the churchyard, and be interred in the evening."

A spot was fixed upon in a distant corner of the churchyard, far from the other tombs. No priest attended, and the coffin was lowered without any religious service. Notwithstanding Hatfield's various and complicated enormities, his untimely end excited considerable commiseration. His manners were extremely polished and insinuating, and he was possessed of qualities which might have rendered him an ornament to society.

The unfortunate Mary of Buttermere went from home to avoid the impertinent visits of unfeeling curiosity. She was much affected; and, indeed, without supposing that any part of her former attachment remained, it is impossible that she could view his tragical fate with indifference. When her father and mother heard that Hatfield had certainly been hanged, they both exclaimed, "God be thanked!"

On the day of his condemnation, Wordsworth and Coleridge passed through Carlisle, and endeavoured to obtain an interview with him. Wordsworth succeeded; but, for some unknown reason, the prisoner steadily refused to see Coleridge; a caprice which could not be penetrated. It was true that he had, during his whole residence at Keswick, avoided Coleridge with a solicitude which had revived the original suspicions against him in some quarters, after they had generally subsided. However, if not him, Coleridge saw and examined his very interesting papers. These were chiefly letters from women whom he had injured, pretty much in the same way, and by the same impostures, as he had recently practised in Cumberland. Great was the emotion of Coleridge when he afterwards recurred to these letters, and bitter —almost vindictive—was the indignation with which he spoke of Hatfield. One set of letters appeared to have been written under too certain a knowledge of his villany towards the individual to whom they were addressed; though still relying on some possible remains of humanity, or perhaps (the poor writer might think) on some lingering relics of affection for herself.

The other set was even more distressing; they were written under the first conflicts of suspicions, alternately repelling with warmth the gloomy doubts which were fast arising, and then yielding to their afflicting evidence; raving in one page under the misery of alarm, in another courting the delusions of hope, and luring back the perfidious deserter—here resigning herself to despair, and there again labouring to show that all might yet be well. Coleridge said often, in looking back upon that frightful exposure of human guilt and misery, that the man who, when pursued by these heart-rending apostrophes, and with this litany of anguish sounding in his ears, from despairing women, and from famishing children, could yet find it possible to enjoy the calm pleasures of a lake tourist, and deliberately to hunt for the picturesque, must have been a fiend of that order which, fortunately, does not often emerge amongst men.

It is painful to remember that, in those days, amongst the multitudes who ended their career in the same ignominious way, and the majority for offences connected with the forgery of bank notes, there must have been a considerable number who perished from the very opposite cause; namely, because they felt, too passionately and profoundly for prudence, the claims of those who looked up to them for support. One common scaffold confounds the most flinty hearts and the tenderest. However, in this instance, it was in some measure the heartless part of Hatfield's conduct which drew upon him his ruin; for the Cumberland jury, it has been asserted, declared their unwillingness to hang him for having forged a frank; and both they, and those who refused to aid his escape, when first apprehended, were reconciled to this harshness entirely by what they had heard of his conduct to their injured young fellow-countrywoman.

She, meantime, under the name of the Beauty of Buttermore, became an object of interest to all England. Dramas and melo-dramas were produced in the London theatres upon her story; and for many a year afterwards, shoals of tourists crowded to the secluded lake and the little homely cabaret, which had been the scene of her brief romance. It was fortunate for a person in her distressing situation, that her home was not in a town; the few and simple who had witnessed her imaginary elevation, having little knowledge of worldly feelings, never for an instant connected with her disappointment any sense of the ludicrous, or spoke of it as a calamity to which her vanity might have co-operated. They treated it as unmixed injury, reflecting shame upon nobody but the wicked perpetrator. Hence, without much trial to her womanly sensibilities, she found herself able to resume her situation in the little inn; and this she continued to hold for many years. In that place, and in that capacity, she was seen repeatedly. She was greatly admired, and became the subject of the poet's song; but "sorrow," to use the beautiful language of Ossian, "sorrow, like a cloud on the sun, shaded her soul."

THE BORDER FREEBOOTERS;

OR, A FIGHT IN BORROWDALE.

IN olden time, when the contiguous countries of England and Scotland held no amicable relation to each other, it may well be supposed that the mountain ridges forming the line of demarcation between the two territories would frequently be the scene of fierce contention between a rival people. The proximity of the English and Scots in the neighbourhood of the border line, and the inoperative character of the laws, arising from the disorders of the feudal system, which filled both countries with chiefs and petty governors, eager, and sufficiently powerful, to make aggressions and reprisals on each other, are of themselves a sufficient explanation of the causes which led to those continued strifes called the Border warfare. The deep enmity of the hostile parties towards each other overthrew, in a good measure, all moral obligation and honourable feeling.

Incursions were frequently made from the north, less for the purpose of contention in arms, than for committing depredations on cattle and property. Hence the name of freebooters came to be applied to the Border clans, and ultimately with much justice; for in course of time it was deemed matter of indifference by either party whether they preyed on their rival neighbours, or on their own countrymen. Instances are, however, on record in which the Border feuds were distinguished by a romantic and chivalrous feeling, that may well be supposed to have animated great and noble minds, in an age when the most powerful sceptre was the sword, and martial prowess the most estimable quality of mankind:—

> "Those were the days, the olden days
>   When Border feuds ran high,
> And the men of the North ofttimes sallied forth
>   On deeds of chivalry.
>
> O! heaven gie rest to the souls of a'
>   Wha lived in those times o' disorder;
> There were gude men and brave in the olden day,
>   On baith sides o' the Border."

Summoning forth "far forgotten things," we will refer to a desperate struggle between two rival clans of Border freebooters, under the stupendous rocks of Honister Crag and Yew Crag.

Late in the evening, at the autumnal season of a year over which passing centuries have thrown a darkening veil, the weary and harassed Borderers of Borrowdale were summoned together by the sound of the slogan, or war-cry of their band. The scouts, who had been sent forth in different directions, to give timely notice of any hostile approaches, returned to their chief, who sat ruminating by his watch-fire, on a neighbouring mountain, and reported the sudden irruption of the Scottish clan, that had swept before them a rich booty of cattle, lying at the foot of Borrowdale hawse. By passing in small companies through well-reconnoitred passes of the mountains, the Scots had contrived to elude the observation of the night guard, till their whole force had again united. They then divided into two companies, one of which drove their booty towards the frontier, and the other remained to protect the rear, and baffle their opponents, if they attempted pursuit. The war-shout of the despoiled clan rung through the mountains, and the Cumberland men repaired one and all to their chief, each one mounted on his pricker—a name applied to their small horses—which were both fleet and sufficiently spirited to overcome a laborious ascent into the hills.

Among the Scottish freebooters none were found possessed of greater skill and daring, in the management of their predatory excursions, than the Græmes. This clan it was who had undertaken and accomplished the capture of Borrowdale, which even in those days of enterprise, was looked upon as an astonishing instance of successful temerity. These troopers were commanded by the younger Græme, a bold, hardy chieftain; and his aged father, the Ossian of the clan, followed in all their expeditions to infuse warlike feeling into their hearts, by reciting "the tale of other times," and the bold enterprises of his past days, when the feebleness of age had not arrived.

All the Border clans cherished feelings of deadly animosity against each other; and this hereditary hate was even greater than their desire for plunder. When the division of the Highland band, under the direction of the two Græmes, had succeeded in diverting the enemy from the track which their comrades had taken, they separated among the hills, there to wait the signal, when a favourable opportunity should present for rushing down in all their strength upon the Cumberland men, and working out the measure of their hatred against them.

After fruitless attempts to recover the spoils which had been wrested from them, the English Borderers resolved to retaliate on the Scottish frontier; and, accordingly, collecting all their power, commenced their march through the desolate region of Borrowdale. Information was speedily conveyed to the younger Græme, that the enemy were approaching. The appointed signal was then given, and the Highlanders once more crowded round their leader. The Scottish chief determined to suspend his attack till the enemy should arrive in the defile between Honister Crag and Yew Crag, when his followers would have the advantage of assailing their foe from the overhanging precipices. They marched along in single rank, through the passes of the mountains, towards the appointed spot, singing their favourite war-song:—

> "Sons of the mountain chief, on to the battle-field!
> Clansmen and Highlanders, grasp ye the sword and shield;
> On the rock or in defile, we'll not be ensnared,
> When the foe is awaiting, are we not prepared?
>
> On, let us meet them, our bucklers shall cover us;
> Our refuge the hills, and heaven's vault over us:
> O'er the steep of the crag, down the side of the scar,
> Let us rush on the foe, in the thunder of war.
>
> Their bugles sound cheerly: Behold them advancing!
> With waving of plumes, and their chargers all prancing;
> Yet the mountains that ring to their proud horses' tread,
> They shall echo ere long to the fall of the dead!"

The Highlanders concealed themselves behind the rocky fragments strewn on the side of Yew Crag, till the English, advancing at a rapid rate, had reached the point in Gatesgarthdale, which lay directly opposite to their ambuscade. Young Græme sprung on his feet, and waved his claymore towards the enemy. The signal was answered by a volley of musketry from the hill; and instantly several horses, without riders, flew through the defile. The elder Græme singled forth the English leader. Sinking on one knee, he raised his musket with deadly certainty, and ere the sound of the death-shot could reach his victim, the white steed that bore him was left unfettered by the rein.

Furious at the loss of their leader, the troopers wheeled their horses round the precipice on which the Græmes and a few of their followers were stationed; and before the remainder of the Highland band could afford succour, the younger Græme, together with several of his clan, had met the death of heroes. The English then dashed forward on their expedition, not caring to continue the battle under the disadvantages of their position.

The Highlanders gathered round their fallen leader, and raised loud lament for the warrior, whose blood was streaming in their view. The old chieftain gazed wildly on his son; and his frame, which seventy winters had not palsied, shook with tremor. The body was laid in an opening on the hill-side, and every clansman brought a fragment of rock, to raise a rude memorial to his chief. On the summit of the pile they placed his bonnet, shield, and claymore, that neither friend nor foe should thereafter pass it with irreverence.

JOSSY WITH WHIPS.

A PARISH CHARACTER.

JOSEPH ROBINSON, better known by the name of "Jossy with Whips," was a well-known character in the parish of Orton in Westmorland. He had his regular rounds, which he constantly travelled; and his accustomed houses, where his never-failing alms was duly received by this self-instituted collector.

Some are still living who can recollect the harmless idiot and all his singular accoutrements. He never appeared without six or eight whips in his hands: a little stick, with a piece of string attached to the end of it, would any time supply honest Joseph with an excellent whip. A piece of an old coat, tied to his body with a hayband, was his usual upper garment; his legs were usually covered with haybands, tier above tier; and a profusion of hemp strings, in his opinion, adorned his person. These simple ornaments were to Joseph as dear and as honourable as the red and blue ribbons which are so anxiously struggled for by his fellows in the higher walks of life. In his hat he wore a fox's brush and peacock feathers, thus aping the fancied splendour of eastern magnificence.

Jossy was a quiet, inoffensive being; and the farmers through all the south of Westmorland would as soon have thought of neglecting any of their just debts, as of refusing the accustomed donation made to him. An out-house was his usual place of lodging; and habit had rendered this so natural to him, that a bed never entered his circumscribed ideas.

After Joseph, like his intelligent fellow-mortals, had been consigned to his "narrow house," a young man, in the parish of Orton, composed the following elegy to his memory:—

"Beneath this lowly, grass-encircled spot,
Lie the remains of Joseph of the Knot.
Death, grisly tyrant, no distinction shows
'Twixt him who all, and him who nothing knows.
Yes, ye! ye mighty sons of boasted wit!
All—all, like Joseph, must to death submit.
Though on his fingers many a ring he bore,
And round his brow the gaudy honours wore,
For him his plumes although the peacock shed,
And reynard's brush graced Joseph's hoary head;

Though armed with whips he constantly appeared,
Death mocked his honours, nor his armour feared.
But ah! despise not Joseph's humble lot—
His life so mean—his death so soon forgot:
In the last day—that great decisive day,
When death shall yield his temporary prey—
By lords, by kings, his fate may be desired—
Where nothing's given, nothing is required."

EMMA AND SIR EGLAMORE.

A LEGEND OF ULLSWATER.

ABOUT a quarter of a mile from Lyulph's Tower, a hunting seat of the late Duke of Norfolk, on the banks of Ullswater, is a lonely brook, the Airey or Aira, which, at Aira Force, falls over the rocks a height of 80 feet, into a beautiful and deep glen, covered with luxuriant foliage of fern and sweet-scented hawthorns. A picturesque bridge unites the precipitous rocks down which the foaming torrent pursues its ceaseless course.

This beautiful waterfall is the scene of the touching legend of the "Somnambulist," which has been versified by Wordsworth. The tale is, that Emma, a beautiful lady, betrothed to one Sir Eglamore, was walking in her sleep on the banks of the fall; and that her lover, who had unexpectedly returned after a long absence—so long as to have affected her health—was struck with the apparition of the maid, who had become subject to night wanderings. He watched her for some time plucking the twigs from the trees, and casting them into the stream, uncertain whether she were a real object, or a mere phantom of his imagination. He touched her, and, suddenly breaking her slumber, the affrighted maid shrieked, and, starting back, fell down the rocks into the stream below. The knight plunged in after her, and rescued her; but, though consciousness returned for a short period, and she recognised him, she expired within a few minutes upon the bank. The heart-broken knight built a cell upon the edge of the fall, and lived there in solitude for several years, shunning all intercourse with the world.

List, ye who pass by Lyulph's Tower
  At eve, how softly then
Doth Aira Force, that torrent hoarse,
  Speak from the woody glen!
Fit music for a solemn vale!
  And holier seems the ground
To him who catches on the gale
The spirit of a mournful tale,
  Embodied in the sound.

Not far from that fair sight whereon
  The pleasure-house is reared,
As story says, in antique days,
  A stern-brow'd houseappeared;
Foil to a jewel rich in light

There set, and guarded well;
Cage for a bird of plumage bright,
Sweet voiced, nor wishing for a flight
Beyond her native dell.

To win this bright bird from her cage,
To make this gem their own,
Came barons bold, with store of gold,
And knights of high renown;
But one she prized, and only one;
Sir Eglamore was he;
Full happy season, when was known,
Ye dales and hills! to you alone
Their mutual loyalty.

Known chiefly, Aira! to thy glen,
The brook, and bowers of holly;
Where passion caught, what nature taught,
That all but love is folly;
Where fact and fancy stooped to play,
Doubt came not, nor regret,
To trouble hours that wing their way,
As if through an immortal day,
Whose sun could never set.

But in old times love dwelt not long
Sequester'd with repose;
Best throve the fire of chaste desire,
Fanned by the breath of foes.
"A conquering lance is beauty's test,
And proves the lover true;"
So spake Sir Eglamore, and pressed
The drooping Emma to his breast,
And looked a blind adieu.

They parted,—Well with him it fared
Through wide-spread regions errant;
A knight of proof in love's behoof,
The thirst of fame his warrant:
And she her happiness can build
On woman's quiet hours;
Though faint, compared with spear and shield,
The solace beads and masses yield,
And needlework and flowers.

Yet blest was Emma when she heard
  Her champion's praise recounted;
Though brain would swim, and eyes grow dim,
  And high her blushes mounted;
Or when a bold heroic lay
  She warbled from full heart;
Delightful blossoms for the May
Of absence! but they will not stay,
  Born only to depart.

Hope wanes with her, while lustre fills
  Whatever path he chooses;
As if his orb, that owns no curb,
  Received the light hers loses.
He comes not back; an ampler space
  Requires for nobler deeds;
He ranges on from place to place,
Till of his doings is no trace,
  But what her fancy breeds.

His fame may spread, but in the past
  Her spirit finds its centre;
Clear sight she has of what he was,
  And that would now content her.
"Still is he my devoted knight?"
  The tear in answer flows;
Month falls on month with heavier weight;
Day sickens round her, and the night
  Is empty of repose.

In sleep she sometimes walked abroad,
  Deep sighs with quick words blending,
Like that pale queen, whose hands are seen
  With fancied spots contending;
But she is innocent of blood:
  The moon is not more pure
That shines aloft, while through thewood
She threads her way, the sounding flood
  Her melancholy lure.

While 'mid the fern-brake sleeps the doe,
  And owls alone are waking,
In white arrayed glides on the maid,
  The downward pathway taking,

That leads her to the torrent's side,
   And to a holly bower;
By whom on this still night descried?
By whom in that lone place espied?
   By thee, Sir Eglamore!

A wandering ghost, so thinks the knight,
   His coming step has thwarted,
Beneath the boughs that heard their vows,
   Within whose shade they parted.
Hush, hush, the busy sleeper see!
   Perplexed her fingers seem,
As if they from the holly tree
Green twigs would pluck, as rapidly
   Flung from her to the stream.

What means the spectre? Why intent
   To violate the tree,
Thought Eglamore, by which I swore
   Unfading constancy?
Here am I, and to-morrow's sun,
   To her I left, shall prove
That bliss is ne'er so surely won
As when a circuit has been run
   Of valour, truth, and love.

So from the spot whereon he stood
   He moved with stealthy pace;
And, drawing nigh with his living eye,
   He recognised the face:
And whispers caught, and speeches small,
   Some to the green-leaved tree,
Some mutter'd to the torrent-fall:—
"Roar on, and bring him with thy call;
   I heard, and so may he!"

Soul-shattered was the knight, nor knew
   If Emma's ghost it were,
Or bodying shade, or if the maid
   Her very self stood there.
He touched; what followed who shall tell?
   The soft touch snapped the thread
Of slumber—shrieking back she fell,
The stream it whirled her down the dell

Along its foaming bed.

In plunged the knight!—when on firm ground
The rescued maiden lay;
Her eyes grew bright with blissful light,
Confusion passed away;
She heard, ere to the throne of grace
Her faithful spirit flew,
His voice—beheld his speaking face;
And, dying, from his own embrace,
She felt that he was true.

So was he reconciled to life:
Brief words may speak the rest;
Within the dell he built a cell,
And there was sorrow's guest;
In hermit's weeds repose he found,
From vain temptations free,
Beside the torrent dwelling, bound
By one deep heart-controlling sound,
And awed to piety.

Wild stream of Aira, hold thy course,
Nor fear memorial lays,
Where clouds that spread in solemn shade,
Are edged with golden rays!
Dear art thou to the light of heaven,
Though minister of sorrow;
Sweet is thy voice at pensive even;
And thou, in lovers' hearts forgiven,
Shalt take thy place with Yarrow.

THE BRIDAL OF TRIERMAIN.

A LEGEND OF THE VALE OF ST. JOHN.

IN travelling from Ambleside to Keswick, after passing Wythburn Chapel, the high road winds by the base of Helvellyn and the margin of the Lake of Thirlmere, or Leatheswater, which latter it afterwards leaves by a very steep ascent, exhibiting, in all their grandeur, the Fells of Borrowdale. Arrived at the top of this ascent, a very exquisite landscape presents itself below, extending over the Vale of Legberthwaite; or, more euphoniously and modernly, the Vale of St. John's.

In the midst of this valley is a fantastic pile of rocks, which, from their resemblance to the walls and towers of a dilapidated and time-worn fortress, are known as the Castle Rock. Hutchinson, in his *Excursion to the Lakes*, describes this singular scene with much poetic feeling. "We now gained the Vale of St. John's," he says, "a very narrow dell, hemmed in by mountains, through which a small brook makes many meanderings, washing little enclosures of grass-ground, which stretch up the rising of the hills. In the widest part of the dale you are struck with the appearance of an ancient ruined castle, which seems to stand upon the summit of a little mount, the mountains around forming an amphitheatre. This massive bulwark shows a front of various towers, and makes an awful, rude, and Gothic appearance, with its lofty turrets and ragged battlements; we traced the galleries, the bending arches, the buttresses. The greatest antiquity stands characterised in its architecture; the inhabitants near it assert it is an antediluvian structure.

"The traveller's curiosity is roused, and he prepares to make a nearer approach, when that curiosity is put upon the rack by his being assured that, if he advances, certain genii who govern the place, by virtue of their supernatural art and necromancy, will strip it of all its beauties, and, by enchantment, transform the magic walls. The vale seems adapted for the habitation of such beings; its gloomy recesses and retirements look like haunts of evil spirits. There was no delusion in the report; we were soon convinced of its truth; for this piece of antiquity, so venerable and noble in its aspect, as we drew near changed its figure and proved no other than a shaken massive pile of rocks, which stand in the midst of this little vale, disunited from the adjoining mountains, and have so much the real form and resemblance of a castle, that they bear the name of the Castle Rocks of St. John."

"The inhabitants to this day," says Mackay, "believe these rocks to be an antediluvian structure, and assert that the traveller, whose curiosity is aroused, will find it impossible to approach them, as the guardian genii of the place transform the walls and battlements into naked rocks when any one draws near." Nothing, in the whole range of mythological fable, could be more beautiful than this popular superstition, which ascribes the disappearance of "the castle," on a near approach, to supernatural agency. Frigid philosophy would say, these fragments of rock, when viewed from afar, bear strong resemblance to an old fortress; but on approaching nearer the illusion vanishes, and they are found to be a shapeless mass of stone. Poetry clothes this fact in beautiful imagery; she warns the intruder to survey the structure at a distance; for should he have the temerity to advance upon it, the incensed genii of the place will, by spells "of power to cheat the eye with blear illusion," transform its fair proportions into a mis-shapen pile of rocks. This pleasing fiction emanated from the same poetical spirit that wrought, in the elder days of Greece, the splendid fable of Aurora, in her saffron-coloured robe, opening the gates of the morning to the chariot of the sun.

The genius of Sir Walter Scott has rendered the beautiful Vale of St. John classic ground, by having selected it for the principal scene of his "Bridal of Triermain." This is purely a tale of chivalry of Arthur's days, when midnight fairies danced the maze; and it is at the fantastic Castle Rock that Sir Walter represents King Arthur's amorous dalliance with its fairy inhabitants in their halls of enchantment, when he was on his way to Carlisle. Our limits will not admit the whole of "The Bridal of Triermain." We give, however, such portions as will sufficiently connect the thread of the narrative, in which it will be observed that Sir Roland de Vaux, the Baron of Tremain, is introduced. This branch of Vaux, with its collateral alliances, is now represented by the family of Braddyl, of Conishead Priory, near Furness Abbey.

THE BRIDAL OF TRIERMAIN.

Where is the Maiden of mortal strain,
That may match with the Baron of Trierman?
She must be lovely, and constant, and kind,
Holy and pure, and humble of mind,
Blithe of cheer and gentle of mood,
Courteous, and generous, and noble ofblood—
Lovely as the sun's first ray
When it breaks the clouds of an Aprilday;
Constant and true as the widow'd dove,
Kind as a minstrel that sings of love;
Pure as the fountain in rocky cave,
Where never sunbeam kissed the wave;
Humble as maiden that loves in vain,
Holy as hermit's vesper strain;

Gentle as breeze that but whispers and dies,
Yet blithe as the light leaves that dance in its sighs;
Courteous as monarch the morn he is crowned,
Generous as spring-dews that bless the glad ground;
Noble her blood as the currents that met
In the veins of the noblest Plantagenet;
Such must her form be, her mood, and her strain,
That shall match with Sir Roland of Triermain.

Sir Roland de Vaux he hath laid him to sleep,
His blood it was fevered, his breathing was deep.
He had been pricking against the Scot,
The foray was long and the skirmish hot;
His dinted helm and his buckler's plight
Bore token of a stubborn fight.

All in the castle must hold them still,
Harpers must lull him to his rest,
With the slow soft tunes he loves the best,
Till sleep sink down upon his breast,
Like the dew on a summer hill.

It was the dawn of an autumn day,
The sun was struggling with frost-fog gray,
That like a silvery crape was spread
Round Skiddaw's dim and distant head,
And faintly gleamed each painted pane
Of the lordly halls of Triermain,
When that Baron bold awoke.
Starting he woke, and loudly did call,
Rousing his menials in bower and hall,
While hastily he spoke.

"Hearken, my minstrels! Which of ye all
Touched his harp with that dying fall,
So sweet, so soft, so faint,
It seem'd an angel's whisper'd call
To an expiring saint?
And hearken, my merry-men! What time or where
Did she pass, that maid with her heavenly brow,
With her look so sweet and her eyes so fair,
And her graceful step and her angel air,
And the eagle-plume in her dark-brown hair,
That pass'd from my bower e'en now!"

Answer'd him Richard de Bretville; he
Was chief of the Baron's minstrelsy—
"Silent, noble chieftain, we
Have sat since midnight close,
When such lulling sounds as the brooklet sings,
Murmur'd from our melting strings,
And hush'd you to repose,
Had a harp-note sounded here,
It had caught my watchful ear,
Although it fell as faint and shy
As bashful maiden's half-formed sigh,
When she thinks her lover near."
Answer'd Philip of Fasthwaite tall,
He kept guard in the outer-hall—
"Since at eve our watch took post,
Not a foot has thy portal cross'd;
Else had I heard the steps, though low,
And light they fell, as when earth receives,
In morn of frost, the wither'd leaves
That drop when no winds blow."—

"Then come thou thither, Henry, my page,
Whom I saved from the sack of Hermitage,
When that dark castle, tower, and spire,
Rose to the skies a pile of fire,
And redden'd all the Nine-stane Hill,
And the shrieks of death, that wildly broke
Through devouring flame and smothering smoke,
Made the warrior's heart-blood chill.
The trustiest thou of all my train,
My fleetest courser thou must rein,
And ride to Lyulph's tower,
And from the Baron of Trierman
Greet well that Sage of power.
He is sprung from Druid sires,
And British bards that tuned their lyres
To Arthur's and Pendragon's praise,
And his who sleeps at Dunmailraise.[17]

Gifted like his gifted race,
He the characters can trace,
Graven deep in elder time
Upon Helvellyn's cliffs sublime:

Sign and sigil well doth he know,
And can bode of weal and woe,
Of kingdoms' fall, and fate of wars,
From mystic dreams and course ofstars.
He shall tell if middle earth
To that enchanting shape gave birth,
Or if 'twas but an airy thing,
Such as fantastic slumbers bring,
Fram'd from the rainbow's varying dyes,
Or fading tints of western skies.
For, by the blessed rood I swear,
If that fair form breathe vital air,
No other maiden by my side
Shall ever rest De Vaux's bride!"

The faithful Page he mounts his steed,
And soon he cross'd green Irthing's mead,
Dash'd o'er Kirkoswald's verdant plain,
And Eden barr'd his course in vain.
He pass'd red Penrith's Table round,[18]
For feats of chivalry renown'd,
Left Mayburgh's mound[19] and stones of power,
By Druids raised in magic hour,
And traced the Eamont's winding way,
Till Ulfo's lake[20] beneath him lay.

Onward he rode, the pathway still
Winding betwixt the lake andhill;
Till, on the fragment of a rock,
Struck from its base by lightning shock,
He saw the hoary sage:
The silver moss and lichen twined,
With fern and deer-hair check'd andlined,
A cushion fit for age;
And o'er him shook theaspin-tree,
A restless rustling canopy.

Then sprung young Henry from his selle,
And greeted Lyulph grave,
And then his master's tale didtell,
And then for counsel crave.
The Man of Years mused long and deep,
Of time's lost treasures taking keep,

And then, as rousing from a sleep,
His solemn answer gave.
"That maid is born of middle earth,
And may of man be won,
Though there have glided since her birth
Five hundred years and one.
But where's the knight in all the north,
That dare the adventure follow forth,
So perilous to knightly worth,
In the valley of St. John?
Listen, youth, to what I tell,
And bind it on thy memory well;
Nor muse that I commence the rhyme
Far distant 'mid the wrecks of time.
The mystic tale, by bard and sage,
Is handed down from Merlin's age."

LYULPH'S TALE.

"King Arthur has ridden from merry Carlisle,
When Pentecost was o'er:
He journey'd like errant-knight the while,
And sweetly the summer sun did smile
On mountain, moss, and moor.
Above his solitary track
Rose huge Blencathara's ridgy back,
Amid whose yawning gulfs the sun
Cast umber'd radiance red and dun,
Though never sunbeam could discern
The surface of that sable tarn,[21]
In whose black mirror you may spy
The stars, while noontide lights the sky.
The gallant King he skirted still
The margin of that mighty hill;
Rock upon rocks incumbent hung,
And torrents, down the gullies flung,
Join'd the rude river that brawl'd on,
Recoiling now from crag and stone,
Now diving deep from human ken,
And raving down its darksome glen.
The Monarch judged this desert wild,

With such romantic ruin piled,
Was theatre by nature's hand
For feat of high achievement plann'd.

"He rode, till over down and dell
The shade more broad and deeper fell;
And though around the mountain's head
Flow'd streams of purple, and gold, and red,
Dark at the base, unblest by beam,
Frown'd the black rocks, and roar'd thestream.
With toil the King his way pursued
By lonely Threlkeld's waste and wood,
Till on his course obliquely shone
The narrow valley of Saint John,
Down sloping to the western sky,
Where lingering sunbeams love to lie.
Right glad to feel those beams again,
The King drew up his charger's rein;
With gauntlet raised he screen'd his sight,
As dazzled with the level light,
And, from beneath his glove of mail,
Scann'd at his ease the lovely vale,
While 'gainst the sun his armour bright
Gleam'd ruddy like the beacon's light.

"Paled in by many a lofty hill,
The narrow dale lay smooth and still,
And, down its verdant bosom led,
A winding brooklet found its bed.
But, midmost of the vale, a mound
Arose with airy turrets crown'd,
Buttress, and rampire's circling bound,
    And mighty keep and tower;
Seem'd some primeval giant's hand,
The castle's massive walls had plann'd,
A ponderous bulwark to withstand
    Ambitious Nimrod's power.
Above the moated entrance slung,
The balanced drawbridge tremblinghung,
    As jealous of a foe;
Wicket of oak, as iron hard,
With iron studded, clench'd, and barr'd,
And prong'd portcullis, join'd to guard

The gloomy pass below.
But the gray walls no banners crown'd,
Upon the watch-tower's airy round,
No warder stood his horn to sound,
No guard beside the bridge was found,
And, where the Gothic gateway frown'd,
Glanced neither bill nor bow.

"Beneath the castle's gloomy pride,
In ample round did Arthur ride
Three times; nor living thing he spied,
Nor heard a living sound,
Save that, awakening from her dream,
The owlet now began to scream,
In concert with the rushing stream,
That wash'd the battled mound.
He lighted from his goodly steed,
And he left him to graze on bank and mead;
And slowly he climb'd the narrow way
That reached the entrance grim and gray,
And he stood the outward arch below,
And his bugle-horn prepared to blow,
In summons blithe and bold,
Deeming to rouse from iron sleep
The guardian of this dismal Keep,
Which well he guess'd the hold
Of wizard stern, or goblin grim,
Or pagan of gigantic limb,
The tyrant of the wold.

"The ivory bugle's golden tip
Twice touch'd the Monarch's manly lip,
And twice his hand withdrew.
—Think not but Arthur's heart was good!
His shield was cross'd by the blessed rood,
Had a pagan host before him stood,
He had charged them through and through;
Yet the silence of that ancient place
Sunk on his heart, and he paused a space
Ere yet his horn he blew.
But, instant as its 'larum rung,
The castle gate was open flung,
Portcullis rose with crashing groan

Full harshly up its groove of stone;
The balance-beams obey'd the blast,
And down the trembling drawbridge cast;
The vaulted arch before him lay,
With nought to bar the gloomy way,
And onward Arthur paced, with hand
On Caliburn's[22] resistless brand.

"A hundred torches, flashing bright,
Dispelled at once the gloomy night
That lour'd along the walls,
And show'd the King's astonish'd sight
The inmates of the halls.
Nor wizard stern nor goblin grim,
Nor giant huge of form and limb,
Nor heathen knight, was there;
But the cressets, which odours flung aloft,
Show'd by their yellow light and soft,
A band of damsels fair.
Onward they came, like summer wave
That dances to the shore;
An hundred voices welcome gave,
And welcome o'er and o'er!
An hundred lovely hands assail
The bucklers of the monarch's mail,
And busy labour'd to unhasp
Rivet of steel and iron clasp.
One wrapp'd him in a mantle fair,
And one flung odours on his hair;
His short curl'd ringlets one smooth'd down,
One wreathed them with a myrtle-crown.
A bride upon her wedding-day,
Was tended ne'er by troop so gay.

"Loud laugh'd they all,—the King, in vain,
With questions task'd the giddy train;
Let him entreat, or crave, or call,
'Twas one reply—loud laugh'd they all.
Then o'er him mimic chains they fling,
Framed of the fairest flowers of spring.
While some their gentle force unite,
Onward to drag the wondering knight,
Some, bolder, urge his pace with blows,

Dealt with the lily or the rose.
Behind him were in triumph borne
The warlike arms he late had worn.
Four of the train combined to rear
The terrors of Tintadgel's spear;[23]
Two, laughing at their lack of strength,
Dragg'd Caliburn in cumbrous length;
One, while she aped a martial stride,
Placed on her brows the helmet's pride;
Then scream'd, 'twixt laughter and surprise,
To feel its depth o'erwhelm her eyes.
With revel-shout, and triumph-song,
Thus gaily march'd the giddy throng.

"Through many a gallery and hall
They led, I ween, their royal thrall;
At length, beneath a fair arcade
Their march and song at once they staid.
The eldest maiden of the band,
(The lovely maid was scarce eighteen,)
Raised, with imposing air, her hand,
And reverent silence did command,
On entrance of their Queen,
And they were mute—But as a glance
They steal on Arthur's countenance
Bewilder'd with surprise,
Their smother'd mirth again 'gan speak,
In archly dimpled chin and cheek,
And laughter-lighted eyes.

"The attributes of those high days
Now only live in minstrel-lays;
Nor Nature, now exhausted, still
Was then profuse of good and ill.
Strength was gigantic, valour high,
And wisdom soar'd beyond the sky,
And beauty had such matchless beam
As lights not now a lover's dream.
Yet e'en in that romantic age,
Ne'er were such charms by mortal seen,
As Arthur's dazzled eyes engage,
When forth on that enchanted stage,
With glittering train of maid and page,

Advanced the castle's Queen!
While up the hall she slowly pass'd,
Her dark eye on the King she cast,
That flash'd expression strong;
The longer dwelt that lingering look,
Her cheek the livelier colour took,
And scarce the shame-faced King could brook
The gaze that lasted long.
A sage, who had that look espied,
Where kindling passion strove with pride,
Had whisper'd, 'Prince, beware!
From the chafed tiger rend the prey,
Rush on the lion when at bay,
Bar the fell dragon's blighted way,
But shun that lovely snare!'—

"At once, that inward strife suppress'd,
The dame approach'd her warlike guest,
With greeting in that fair degree,
Where female pride and courtesy
Are blended with such passing art
As awes at once and charms the heart.
A courtly welcome first she gave,
Then of his goodness 'gan to crave
Construction fair and true
Of her light maidens' idle mirth,
Who drew from lonely glens their birth,
Nor knew to pay to stranger worth
And dignity their due;
And then she pray'd that he would rest
That night her castle's honour'd guest.
The Monarch meetly thanks express'd;
The banquet rose at her behest,
With lay and tale, and laugh and jest,
Apace the evening flew.

"The lady sate the Monarch by,
Now in her turn abash'd and shy,
And with indifference seem'd to hear
The toys he whisper'd in her ear.
Her bearing modest was and fair,
Yet shadows of constraint were there,
That show'd an over-cautious care

Some inward thought to hide;
Oft did she pause in full reply,
And oft cast down her large dark eye,
Oft check'd the soft voluptuous sigh,
That heav'd her bosom's pride.

"Another day, another day,
And yet another, glides away!
The Saxon stern, the pagan Dane,
Maraud on Britain's shores again.
Arthur, of Christendom the flower,
Lies loitering in a lady's bower;
The horn, that foemen wont to fear,
Sounds but to wake the Cumbrian deer,
And Caliburn, the British pride,
Hangs useless by a lover's side.

"Another day, another day,
And yet another, glides away!
Heroic plans in pleasure drowned,
He thinks not of the Table Round;
In lawless love dissolved his life,
He thinks not of his beauteous wife:
Better he loves to snatch a flower
From bosom of his paramour,
Than from a Saxon knight to wrest
The honours of his heathen crest;
Better to wreathe, 'mid tresses brown,
The heron's plume her hawk struck down,
Than o'er the altar give to flow
The banners of a Paynim foe.
Thus, week by week, and day by day,
His life inglorious glides away;
But she, that soothes his dream, with fear
Beholds his hour of waking near.

"Three summer months had scantly flown,
When Arthur, in embarrass'd tone,
Spoke of his liegemen and his throne;
Said, all too long had been his stay,
And duties, which a monarch sway,
Duties, unknown to humbler men,
Must tear her knight from Guendolen.

She listened silently the while,
Her mood expressed in bitter smile;
Beneath her eye must Arthur quail,
And oft resume the unfinished tale,
Confessing, by his downcast eye,
The wrong he sought to justify.
He ceased. A moment mute she gazed,
And then her looks to heaven she raised;
One palm her temples veiled, to hide
The tear that sprung in spite of pride;
The other for an instant pressed
The foldings of her silken vest!

"At her reproachful sign and look
The hint the monarch's conscience took.
Eager he spoke—'No, Lady, no!
Deem not of British Arthur so,
Nor think he can deserter prove
To the dear pledge of mutual love.
I swear by sceptre and by sword,
As belted knight and Britain's lord,
That if a boy shall claim my care,
That boy is born a kingdom's heir;
But, if a maiden Fate allows,
To choose that maid a fitting spouse,
A summer-day in lists shall strive
My knights—the bravest knights alive,—
And he, the best and bravest tried,
Shall Arthur's daughter claim for bride.'—
He spoke, with voice resolved and high—
The lady deigned him not reply.

"At dawn of morn, ere on the brake
His matins did a warbler make,
Or stirred his wing to brush away
A single dewdrop from the spray,
Ere yet a sunbeam through the mist,
The castle-battlements had kissed,
The gates revolve, the drawbridge falls,
And Arthur sallies from the walls.
Doff'd his soft garb of Persia's loom,
And steel from spur to helmet-plume,
His Lybian steed full proudly trode,

And joyful neighed beneath his load.
The Monarch gave a passing sigh
To penitence and pleasures by,
When, lo! to his astonished ken,
Appeared the form of Guendolen.

"Beyond the utmost wall she stood,
Attired like huntress of the wood:
Sandalled her feet, her ankles bare,
And eagle-plumage decked her hair;
Firm was her look, her bearing bold,
And in her hand a cup of gold.
'Thou goest!' she said, 'and ne'er again
Must we two meet; in joy or pain.
Full fain would I this hour delay,
Thought weak the wish—yet wilt thou stay?
—No! thou look'st forward. Still attend,—
Part we like lover and like friend.'
She raised the cup—'Not this the juice
The sluggish vines of earth produce;
Pledge we, at parting, in the draught
Which Genii love!'—she said and quaffed;
And strange unwonted lustres fly
From her flushed cheek and sparkling eye.

"The courteous monarch bent him low,
And, stooping down from saddlebow,
Lifted the cup, in act to drink.
A drop escaped the goblet's brink—
Intense as liquid fire from hell,
Upon the charger's neck it fell.
Screaming with agony and fright,
He bolted twenty feet upright—
—The peasant still can show the dint
Where his hoofs lighted on the flint.—
From Arthur's hand the goblet flew,
Scattering a shower of fiery dew,
That burned and blighted where it fell![24]
The frantic steed rushed up the dell,
As whistles from the bow the reed;
Nor bit nor rein could check his speed,
Until he gained the hill;
Then breath and sinew failed apace,

And, reeling from the desperate race,
He stood, exhausted, still.
The Monarch, breathless and amazed,
Back on the fatal castle gazed——
Nor tower nor donjon could he spy,
Darkening against the morning sky;
But, on the spot where once they frowned,
The lonely streamlet brawled around
A tufted knoll, where dimly shone
Fragments of rock and rifted stone.
Musing on this strange hap the while,
The King wends back to fair Carlisle;
And cares, that cumber royal sway,
Wore memory of the past away.

"Full fifteen years, and more, were sped,
Each brought new wreaths to Arthur's head.
Twelve bloody fields, with glory fought,
The Saxons to subjection brought:
Rython, the mighty giant, slain
By his good brand, relieved Bretagne:
The Pictish Gillamore, in fight,
And Roman Lucius, owned his might;
And wide were through the world renowned
The glories of his Table Round.
Each knight, who sought adventurous fame,
To the bold court of Britain came,
And all who suffered causeless wrong,
From tyrant proud or faitour strong,
Sought Arthur's presence to complain,
Nor there for aid implored in vain.

"For this the King, with pomp and pride,
Held solemn court at Whitsuntide,
And summoned Prince and Peer—
All who owed homage for their land,
Or who craved knighthood from his hand,
Or who had succour to demand—
To come from far and near.

"The heralds named the appointed spot,
As Caerleon or Camelot,
Or Carlisle fair and free.

At Penrith, now, the feast was set,
And in fair Eamont's vale were met
    The flower of chivalry.

"When wine and mirth did most abound,
And harpers played their blithest round,
A shrilly trumpet shook the ground,
    And marshals cleared the ring;
A maiden, on a palfrey white,
Heading a band of damsels bright,
Paced through the circle, to alight
    And kneel before the King.
Arthur, with strong emotion, saw
Her graceful boldness checked by awe,
Her dress like huntress of the wold,
Her bow and baldric trapped with gold,
Her sandalled feet, her ankles bare,
And the eagle-plume that decked her hair.
Graceful her veil she backward flung—
The King, as from his seat he sprung,
    Almost cried, 'Guendolen!'
But 'twas a face more frank and wild,
Betwixt the woman and the child,
Where less of magic beauty smiled
    Than of the race of men;
And in the forehead's haughty grace,
The lines of Britain's royal race,
    Pendragon's you might ken.

"Faltering, yet gracefully she said—
'Great Prince! behold an orphan maid,
In her departed mother's name,
A father's vowed protection claim!
The vow was sworn in desert lone,
In the deep valley of St. John.'
At once the King the suppliant raised,
And kissed her brow, her beauty praised;
His vow, he said, should well be kept,
Ere in the sea, the sun was dipped,—
Then conscious glanced upon his queen:
But she, unruffled at the scene,
Of human frailty construed mild,
Looked upon Lancelot and smiled.

"'Up! up! each knight of gallant crest
   Take buckler, spear, and brand!
He that to-day shall bear him best,
   Shall win my Gyneth's hand.
And Arthur's daughter, when a bride,
   Shall bring a noble dower;
Both fair Strath-Clyde and Reged wide,
   And Carlisle town and tower.'
Then might you hear each valiant knight,
   To page and squire that cried,
'Bring my armour bright, and my courser wight!
'Tis not each day that a warrior's might
   May win a royal bride.'
Then cloaks and caps of maintenance
   In haste aside they fling;
The helmets glance, and gleams the lance,
   And the steel-weaved hauberks ring.
Small care had they of their peaceful array,
   They might gather it that wolde;
For brake and bramble glitter'd gay,
   With pearls and cloth of gold.

"Within trumpet sound of the Table Round
   Were fifty champions free,
And they all arise to fight that prize,—
   They all arise but three.
The knights they busied them so fast,
   With buckling spur and belt,
That sigh and look, by ladies cast,
   Were neither seen nor felt.

"From pleading, or upbraiding glance,
   Each gallant turns aside,
And only thought, 'If speeds my lance,
   A queen becomes my bride!
She has fair Strath-Clyde, and Reged wide,
   And Carlisle tower and town;
She is the loveliest maid, beside,
   That ever heired a crown.'
So in haste their coursers they bestride,
   And strike their visors down.

"The champions, arm'd in martial sort,

Have throng'd into the list,
And but three knights of Arthur's court
Are from the tourney miss'd.

"Now caracol'd the steeds in air,
Now plumes and pennons wanton'd fair,
As all around the lists so wide
In panoply the champions ride.
King Arthur saw, with startled eye,
The flower of chivalry march by,
The kingdom's shield in hour of need,
Too late he thought him of the woe
Might from their civil conflict flow;
For well he knew they would not part
Till cold was many a gallant heart.
His hasty vow he 'gan to rue,
And Gyneth then apart he drew;
To her his leading-staff resign'd,
But added caution grave and kind.

"'Thou see'st my child, as promise-bound,
I bid the trump for tourney sound.
Take thou my warder, as the queen
And umpire of the martial scene;
But mark thou this:—as Beauty bright
Is polar star to valiant knight,
As at her word his sword he draws,
His fairest guerdon her applause,
So gentle maid should never ask
Of knighthood vain and dangerous task;
And Beauty's eyes should ever be
Like the twin stars that soothe the sea,
And Beauty's breath should whisper peace,
And bid the storm of battle cease.
I tell thee this, lest all too far
These knights urge tourney into war.
Blithe at the trumpet let them go,
And fairly counter blow for blow:—
No striplings these, who succour need,
For a raised helm or fallen steed.
But, Gyneth, when the strife grows warm,
And threatens death or deadly harm,
Thy sire entreats, thy king commands,

Thou drop the warder from thy hands.
Trust thou thy father with thy fate,
Doubt not he choose thee fitting mate;
Nor be it said, through Gyneth's pride
A rose of Arthur's chaplet died.'

"A proud and discontented glow
O'ershadowed Gyneth's brow of snow;
She put the warder by:—
'Reserve thy boon, my liege,' she said,
'Thus chaffer'd down and limited.
Debased and narrow'd, for a maid,
Of less degree than I.
No petty chief, but holds his heir
At a more honour'd price and rare
Than Britain's King holds me!
Although the sun-burn'd maid, for dower,
Has but her father's rugged tower,
His barren hill and lee.'
King Arthur swore, 'By crown and sword,
As belted Knight, and Britain's lord,
That a whole summer's day should strive
His knights, the bravest knights alive!'—
'Recal thine oath! and to her glen
Poor Gyneth can return agen;
Not on thy daughter will the stain,
That soils thy sword and crown, remain.
But think not she will e'er be bride
Save to the bravest, proved and tried;
Pendragon's daughter will not fear
For clashing sword or splinter'd spear,
Nor shrink though blood should flow.'

"He frown'd and sigh'd, the Monarch bold:—
'I give—what I may not withhold;
For not for danger, dread, or death,
Must British Arthur break his faith.
Too late I mark thy mother's art
Hath taught thee this relentless part.
Use, then, the warder, as thou wilt;
But, trust me, that, if life be spilt,
In Arthur's love, in Arthur's grace,
Gyneth shall lose a daughter's place.'

With that he turn'd his head aside,
Nor brook'd to gaze upon her pride,
As, with the truncheon raised, she sate
The arbitress of mortal fate;
Nor brook'd to mark, in ranks disposed,
How the bold champions stood opposed,
For shrill the trumpet-flourish fell
Upon his ear like passing bell!
Then first from sight of martial fray
Did Britain's hero turn away.

"But Gyneth heard the clangour high,
As hears the hawk the partridge cry.
So well accomplish'd was each knight,
To strike and to defend in fight,
Their meeting was a goodly sight,
While plate and mail held true.
The lists with painted plumes were strown,
Upon the wind at random thrown,
But helm and breastplate bloodless shone,
It seem'd their feather'd crests alone
Should this encounter rue.

"But soon too earnest grew their game,
The spears drew blood, the swords struck flame,
And, horse and man, to ground there came
Knights, who shall rise no more!
Gone was the pride the war that graced,
Gay shields were cleft, and crests defaced,
And steel coats riven, and helms unbraced,
And pennons stream'd with gore.
Gone, too, were fence and fair array,
And desperate strength made deadly way
At random through the bloody fray,
And blows were dealt with headlong sway,
Unheeding where they fell;
And now the trumpet's clamour seem
Like the shrill sea-bird's wailing scream,
Heard o'er the whirlpool's gulfing stream,
The sinking seaman's knell!

"Already gasping on the ground
Lie twenty of the Table Round,

Of chivalry the prime.
Arthur, in anguish, tore away
From head and beard his tresses gray,
And she, proud Gyneth, felt dismay,
And quaked with ruth and fear;
But still she deem'd her mother's shade
Hung o'er the tumult, and forbade
The sign that had the slaughter staid,
And chid the rising tear.
Then Brunor, Taulas, Mador, fell,
Helias the White, and Lionel,
And many a champion more;
Rochemont and Dinadam are down,
And Ferrand of the Forest Brown
Lies gasping in his gore.
Vanoc, by mighty Morolt press'd
Even to the confines of the list,
Young Vanoc of the beardless face
(Fame spoke the youth of Merlin's race),
O'erpower'd at Gyneth's footstool bled,
His heart's-blood died her sandals red.
But then the sky was overcast.
Then howl'd at once a whirlwind's blast,
And, rent by sudden throes,
Yawn'd in mid lists the quaking earth,
And from the gulf,—tremendous birth!—
The form of Merlin rose.

"Sternly the Wizard Prophet eyed
The dreary lists with slaughter dyed,
And sternly raised his hand;—
'Madmen,' he said, 'your strife forbear!
And thou, fair cause of mischief, hear
The doom thy fates demand!
Long shall close in stony sleep
Eyes for ruth that would not weep;
Iron lethargy shall seal
Heart that pity scorn'd to feel.
Yet, because thy mother's art
Warp'd thine unsuspicious heart,
And for love of Arthur's race,
Punishment is blent with grace,

Thou shalt bear thy penance lone
In the valley of Saint John,
And this doom shall overtake thee;
Sleep, until a knight shall wake thee,
For feats of arms as far renown'd
As warrior of the Table Round.
Long endurance of thy slumber
Well may teach the world to number
All their woes from Gyneth's pride,
When the Red Cross champions died.'

"As Merlin speaks, on Gyneth's eye
Slumber's load begins to lie;
Fear and anger vainly strive
Still to keep its light alive.
Twice, with effort and with pause,
O'er her brow her hand she draws;
Twice her strength in vain she tries,
From the fatal chair to rise;
Merlin's magic doom is spoken,
Vanoc's death must now be wroken.
Slow the dark-fringed eyelids fall,
Curtaining each azure ball,
Slowly as on summer eves
Violets fold their dusky leaves.
The weighty baton of command
Now bears down her sinking hand,
On her shoulder droops her head:
Net of pearl and golden thread,
Bursting, gave her locks to flow
O'er her arm and breast of snow.
And so lovely seem'd she there,
Spell-bound in her ivory chair,
That her angry sire, repenting,
Craved stern Merlin for relenting,
And the champions, for her sake,
Would again the contest wake;
Till, in necromantic night,
Gyneth vanish'd from their sight.

"Still she bears her weird alone,
In the Valley of Saint John;
And her semblance oft will seem,

Mingling in a champion's dream,
Of her weary lot to plain,
And crave his aid to burst her chain.
While her wondrous tale was new,
Warriors to her rescue drew,
East and west, and south and north,
From the Liffy, Thames, and Forth.
Most have sought in vain the glen,
Tower nor castle could they ken;
Not at every time or tide,
Nor by every eye descried,
Fast and vigil must be borne,
Many a night in watching worn,
Ere an eye of mortal powers
Can discern those magic towers.
Of the persevering few,
Some from hopeless task withdrew,
When they read the dismal threat
Graved upon the gloomy gate.
Few have braved the yawning door,
And those few return'd no more.
In the lapse of time forgot,
Wellnigh lost is Gyneth's lot;
Sound she sleeps as in the tomb,
Till waken'd by the trump of doom."

THIS IS THE END OF LYULPH'S TALE.

We must now
Resume the legendary strain
Of the bold Knight of Triermain.
That lord, on high adventure bound,
Hath wandered forth alone,
And day and night keeps watchful round
In the valley of Saint John.

When first began his vigil bold,
The moon twelve summer nights was old,
And shone both fair and full;
High in the vault of cloudless blue,
O'er streamlet, dale, and rock, she threw
Her light composed and cool.
Stretched on the brown hill's heathy breast,
Sir Roland eyed the vale;
Chief where, distinguished from the rest,
Those clustering rocks upreared their crest,
The dwelling of the fair distressed,
As told grey Lyulph's tale.
Thus as he lay, the lamp of night
Was quivering on his armour bright,
In beams that rose and fell,
And danced upon his buckler's boss,
That lay beside him on the moss,
As on a crystal well.

Ever he watch'd, and oft he deemed,
While on the mound the moonlight streamed,
It altered to his eyes;
Fain would he hope the rocks 'gan change
To buttress'd walls their shapeless range,
Fain think, by transmutation strange,
He saw grey turrets rise.
But scarce his heart with hope throbb'd high,
Before the wild illusions fly,
Which fancy had conceived.
For, seen by moon of middle night,
Or by the blaze of noontide bright,
Or by the dawn of morning light,
Or evening's western flame,
In every tide, at every hour,

In mist, in sunshine, and in shower,
The rocks remain'd the same.

Oft has he traced the charmed mound,
Oft climb'd its crest, or paced it round,
Yet nothing might explore,
Save that the crags so rudely piled,
At distance seen, resemblance wild
To a rough fortress bore.
Yet still his watch the Warrior keeps,
Feeds hard and spare, and seldom sleeps,
And drinks but of the well;
Ever by day he walks the hill,
And when the evening gale is chill,
He seeks a rocky cell,
Like hermit poor to bid his bead,
And tell his Ave and his Creed,
Invoking every saint at need,
For aid to burst his spell.

And now the moon her orb has hid,
And dwindled to a silver thread,
Dim seen in middle heaven,
While o'er its curve careering fast,
Before the fury of the blast
The midnight clouds are driven.
The brooklet raved, for on the hills
The upland showers had swoln the rills,
And down the torrents came;
Mutter'd the distant thunder dread,
And frequent o'er the vale was spread
A sheet of lightning flame.
De Vaux, within his mountain cave
(No human step the storm durst brave),
To moody meditation gave
Each faculty of soul,
Till, lull'd by distant torrent sound,
And the sad winds that whistled round,
Upon his thoughts, in musing drown'd,
A broken slumber stole.

Twas then was heard a heavy sound
(Sound, strange and fearful there to hear,

'Mongst desert hills, where, leagues around,
Dwelt but the gorcock and the deer):
As, starting from his couch of fern,
Again he heard, in clangor stern,
That deep and solemn swell,—
Twelve times, in measured tone, it spoke,
Like some proud minster's pealing clock,
Or city's larum bell.
What thought was Roland's first when fell,
In that deep wilderness, the knell
Upon his startled ear?
To slander, warrior, were I loth,
Yet must I hold my minstrel troth,—
It was a thought of fear.

But lively was the mingled thrill
That chased that momentary chill,
For Love's keen wish was there,
And eager Hope, and Valour high,
And the proud glow of Chivalry,
That burn'd to do and dare.
Forth from the cave the Warrior rush'd,
Long ere the mountain-voice was hush'd,
That answer'd to the knell;
For long and far the unwonted sound,
Eddying in echoes round and round,
Was toss'd from fell to fell;
And Glaramara answer flung,
And Grisdale-pike responsive rung,
And Legbert heights their echoes swung,
As far as Derwent's dell.

Forth upon trackless darkness gazed
The Knight, bedeafen'd and amazed,
Till all was hush'd and still,
Save the swoln torrent's sullen roar,
And the night-blast that wildly bore
Its course along the hill.
Then on the northern sky there came
A light, as of reflected flame,
And over Legbert-head,
As if by magic art controll'd,
A mighty meteor slowly roll'd

Its orb of fiery red;
Thou wouldst have thought some demon dire
Came mounted on that car of fire,
To do his errand dread.
Far on the sloping valley's course,
On thicket, rock, and torrent hoarse,
Shingle and Scree, and Fell and Force,
A dusky light arose:
Display'd, yet alter'd was the scene;
Dark rock, and brook of silver sheen,
Even the gay thicket's summer green,
In bloody tincture glows.

De Vaux had mark'd the sunbeams set,
At eve, upon the coronet
Of that enchanted mound,
And seen but crags at random flung,
That, o'er the brawling torrent hung,
In desolation frown'd.
What sees he by that meteor's lour?—
A banner'd castle, keep, and tower,
Return the lurid gleam,
With battled walls and buttress fast,
And barbican and ballium vast,
And airy flanking towers, that cast
Their shadows on the stream.
'Tis no deceit! distinctly clear
Crenell and parapet appear,
While o'er the pile that meteor drear
Makes momentary pause;
Then forth its solemn path it drew,
And fainter yet and fainter grew
Those gloomy towers upon the view,
As its wild light withdraws.

Forth from the cave did Roland rush,
O'er crag and stream, through brier and bush;
Yet far he had not sped,
Ere sunk was that portentous light
Behind the hills, and utter night
Was on the valley spread.
He paused perforce, and blew his horn,
And, on the mountain echoes borne,

Was heard an answering sound,
A wild and lonely trumpet-note,—
In middle air it seemed to float
High o'er the battled mound;
And sounds were heard, as when a guard
Of some proud castle, holding ward,
Pace forth their nightly round.
The valiant Knight of Triermain
Rung forth his challenge-blast again,
But answer came there none;
And 'mid the mingled wind and rain,
Darkling he sought the vale in vain,
Until the dawning shone;
And when it dawn'd, that wondrous sight,
Distinctly seen by meteor-light,
It all had passed away!
And that enchanted mount once more
A pile of granite fragments bore,
As at the close of day.

Steel'd for the deed, De Vaux's heart
Scorn'd from his venturous quest to part,
He walks the vale once more;
But only sees, by night or day,
That shatter'd pile of rocks so gray,
Hears but the torrent's roar.
Till when, through hills of azure borne,
The moon renew'd her silver horn,
Just at the time her waning ray,
Had faded in the dawning day,
A summer mist arose;
Adown the vale the vapours float,
And cloudy undulations moat
That tufted mound of mystic note,
As round its base they close.
And higher now the fleecy tide
Ascends its stern and shaggy side,
Until the airy billows hide
The rock's majestic isle;
It seem'd a veil of filmy lawn,
By some fantastic fairy drawn
Around enchanted pile.

The breeze came softly down the brook,
And sighing as it blew,
The veil of silver mist it shook,
And to De Vaux's eager look
Renew'd that wondrous view,
For, though the loitering vapour braved
The gentle breeze, yet oft it waved
It's mantle's dewy fold:
And still, when shook that filmy screen,
Were towers and bastions dimly seen,
And Gothic battlements between
Their gloomy length unroll'd,
Speed, speed, De Vaux, ere on thine eye
Once more the fleeting vision die!
—The gallant knight can speed
As prompt and light as when the hound
Is opening, and the horn is wound,
Careers the hunter's steed.
Down the steep dell his course amain
Hath rivall'd archer's shaft;
But ere the mound he could attain,
The rocks their shapeless form regain,
And, mocking loud his labour vain,
The mountain spirits laugh'd.
Far up the echoing dell was borne
Their wild unearthly shout of scorn.

Wroth wax'd the Warrior.—"Am I then
Fool'd by the enemies of men,
Like a poor hind, whose homeward way
Is haunted by malicious fay?
Is Triermain become your taunt,
De Vaux your scorn? False fiends, avaunt!"
A weighty curtal-axe he bare;
The baleful blade so bright and square,
And the tough shaft of heben wood,
Were oft in Scottish gore imbrued.
Backward his stately form he drew,
And at the rocks the weapon threw,
Just where one crag's projected crest
Hung proudly balanced o'er the rest,
Hurl'd with main force, the weapon's shock

Rent a huge fragment of the rock,
If by mere strength, 'twere hard to tell,
Or if the blow dissolved some spell,
But down the headlong ruin came,
With cloud of dust and flash of flame.
Down bank, o'er bush, its course was borne,
Crush'd lay the copse, the earth was torn,
Till staid at length, the ruin dread
Cumber'd the torrent's rocky bed,
And bade the waters' high-swoln tide
Seek other passage for its pride.

When ceased that thunder, Triermain
Survey'd the mound's rude front again;
And lo! the ruin had laid bare,
Hewn in the stone, a winding stair,
Whose moss'd and fractured steps might lend
The means the summit to ascend;
And by whose aid the brave De Vaux
Began to scale these magic rocks,
    And soon a platform won,
Where, the wild witchery to close,
Within three lances' length arose
    The Castle of Saint John!
No misty phantom of the air,
No meteor-blazon'd show was there:
In morning splendour, full and fair,
    The massive fortress shone.

Embattled high and proudly tower'd,
Shaded by pond'rous flankers, lower'd
    The portal's gloomy way.
Though for six hundred years and more,
Its strength had brook'd the tempest's roar,
The scutcheon'd emblems which it bore
    Had suffer'd no decay:
But from the eastern battlement
A turret had made sheer descent,
And, down in recent ruin rent,
    In the mid torrent lay.
Else, o'er the castle's brow sublime,
Insults of violence or of time
Unfelt had pass'd away.

In shapeless characters of yore.
The gate this stern inscription bore:—

INSCRIPTION.

"Patience waits the destined day,
Strength can clear the cumber'd way.
Warrior, who hast waited long,
Firm of soul, of sinew strong,
It is given to thee to gaze
On the pile of ancient days.
Never mortal builder's hand
This enduring fabric plann'd;
Sign and sigil, word of power,
From the earth raised keep and tower.
View it o'er, and pace it round,
Rampart, turret, battled mound.
Dare no more! To cross the gate
Were to tamper with thy fate;
Strength and fortitude were vain,
View it o'er—and turn again."—
"That would I," said the warrior bold,
"If that my frame were bent and old,
And my thin blood dropp'd slow and cold
As icicle in thaw;
But while my heart can feel it dance,
Blithe as the sparkling wine of France,
And this good arm wields sword or lance,
I mock these words of awe!"
He said; the wicket felt the sway
Of his strong hand, and straight gave way,
And, with rude crash and jarring bray,
The rusty bolts withdraw;
But o'er the threshold as he strode,
And forward took the vaulted road,
An unseen arm, with force amain,
The ponderous gate flung close again,
And rusted bolt and bar
Spontaneous took their place once more,
While the deep arch with sullen roar
Return'd their surly jar.

"Now closed is the gin and the prey within
By the Rood of Lanercost!
But he that would win the war-wolf's skin,
May rue him of his boast."
Thus muttering, on the Warrior went,
By dubious light down steep descent.

Unbarr'd, unlock'd, unwatch'd, a port
Led to the Castle's outer court:
There the main fortress, broad and tall,
Spread its long range of bower and hall,
And towers of varied size,
Wrought with each ornament extreme,
That Gothic art, in wildest dream
Of fancy, could devise;
But full between the Warrior's way
And the main portal arch, there lay
An inner moat;
Nor bridge nor boat
Affords De Vaux the means to cross
The clear, profound, and silent fosse.
His arms aside in haste he flings,
Cuirass of steel and hauberk rings
And down falls helm, and down the shield,
Rough with the dints of many a field.
Fair was his manly form, and fair
His keen dark eye, and close curl'd hair,
When, all unarm'd, save that the brand
Of well-proved metal graced his hand,
With nought to fence his dauntless breast
But the close gipon's under-vest,
Whose sullied buff the sable stains
Of hauberk and of mail retains,—
Roland De Vaux upon the brim
Of the broad moat stood prompt to swim.

Accoutred thus he dared the tide,
And soon he reached the farther side,
And enter'd soon the Hold,
And paced a hall, whose walls so wide
Were blazon'd all with feats of pride,
By warriors done of old.
In middle lists they counter'd here,

While trumpets seem'd to blow;
And there, in den or desert drear,
They quell'd gigantic foe,
Braved the fierce griffon in his ire,
Or faced the dragon's breath of fire.
Strange in their arms, and strange in face,
Heroes they seem'd of ancient race,
Whose deeds of arms, and race, and name,
Forgotten long by later fame,
Were here depicted, to appal
Those of an age degenerate,
Whose bold intrusion braved their fate
In this enchanted hall.
For some short space, the venturous Knight
With these high marvels fed his sight,
Then sought the chamber's upper end,
Where three broad easy steps ascend
To an arch'd portal door,
In whose broad folding leaves of state
Was framed a wicket window-grate,
And ere he ventured more,
The gallant Knight took earnest view
The grated wicket-window through.

O, for his arms! Of martial weed
Had never mortal Knight such need!—
He spied a stately gallery; all
Of snow-white marble was the wall,
The vaulting, and the floor;
And, contrast strange! on either hand
There stood array'd in sable band
Four maids whom Afric bore;
And each a Lybian tiger led,
Held by as bright and frail a thread
As Lucy's golden hair,
For the leash that bound these monsters dread
Was but of gossamer,
Each Maiden's short barbaric vest,
Left all unclosed the knee and breast,
And limbs of shapely jet;
White was their vest and turban's fold,
On arms and ankles rings of gold

In savage pomp were set;
A quiver on their shoulders lay,
And in their hand an assagay.
Such and so silent stood they there,
That Roland wellnigh hoped
He saw a band of statues rare,
Station'd the gazer's soul to scare;
But, when the wicket oped,
Each grisly beast 'gan upward draw,
Roll'd his grim eye, and spread his claw,
Scented the air, and lick'd his jaw;
While these weird Maids, in Moorish tongue,
A wild and dismal warning sung.

"Rash adventurer, bear thee back!
Dread the spell of Dahomay!
Fear the race of Zaharak,[25]
Daughters of the burning day!

"When the whirlwind's gusts are wheeling,
Ours it is the dance to braid;
Zarah's sands in pillars reeling,
Join the measure that we tread,
When the Moon has donn'd her cloak,
And the stars are red to see,
Shrill when pipes the sad Siroc,
Music meet for such as we.

"Where the shatter'd columns lie,
Showing Carthage once had been,
If the wandering Santon's eye
Our mysterious rites hath seen,—
Oft he cons the prayer of death,
To the nations preaches doom,
'Asrael's brand hath left the sheath!
Moslems, think upon the tomb!'

"Ours the scorpion, ours the snake,
Ours the hydra of the fen,
Ours the tiger of the brake,
All that plagues the sons of men.
Ours the tempest's midnight wrack,
Pestilence that wastes by day—
Dread the race of Zaharak!

Fear the spell of Dahomay!"

Uncouth and strange the accents shrill
Rung those vaulted roofs among,
Long it was ere, faint and still,
Died the far-resounding song.
While yet the distant echoes roll,
The Warrior communed with his soul.
"When first I took this venturous quest,
I swore upon the rood,
Neither to stop, nor turn, nor rest,
For evil or for good.
My forward path too well I ween,
Lies yonder fearful ranks between;
For man unarm'd, 'tis bootless hope
With tigers and with fiends to cope—
Yet, if I turn, what waits me there,
Save famine dire and fell despair?—
Other conclusion let me try,
Since, choose howe'er I list, I die.
Forward, lies faith and knightly fame;
Behind, are perjury and shame.
In life or death I hold my word!"
With that he drew his trusty sword,
Caught down a banner from the wall,
And enter'd thus the fearful hall.

On high each wayward Maiden threw
Her swarthy arm, with wild haloo!
On either side a tiger sprung—
Against the leftward foe he flung
The ready banner, to engage
With tangling folds the brutal rage;
The right-hand monster in mid air
He struck so fiercely and so fair,
Through gullet and through spinal bone
The trenchant blade hath sheerly gone.
His grisly brethren ramp'd and yell'd,
But the slight leash their rage withheld,
Whilst, 'twixt their ranks, the dangerous road
Firmly, though swift, the champion strode.
Safe to the gallery's bound he drew,
Safe pass'd an open portal through;

And when against pursuit he flung
The gate, judge if the echoes rung!
Onward his daring course he bore,
While, mix'd with dying growl and roar,
Wild jubilee and loud hurra
Pursued him on his venturous way.

"Hurra, hurra! Our watch is done!
We hail once more the tropic sun.
Pallid beams of northern day,
Farewell, farewell! Hurra, hurra!

"Five hundred years o'er this cold glen
Hath the pale sun come round again;
Foot of man, till now, hath ne'er
Dared to cross the Hall of Fear.

"Warrior! thou, whose dauntless heart
Gives us from our ward to part.
Be as strong in future trial,
Where resistance is denial.

"Now for Afric's glowing sky,
Zwenga wide and Atlas high,
Zaharak and Dahomay!——
Mount the winds! Hurra, hurra!"

The wizard song at distance died,
   As if in ether borne astray,
While through waste halls and chambers wide
   The Knight pursued his steady way.
Till to a lofty dome he came,
That flash'd with such a brilliant flame,
As if the wealth of all the world
Were there in rich confusion hurl'd.
For here the gold, in sandy heaps,
With duller earth incorporate, sleeps;
Was there in ingots piled, and there
Coin'd badge of empery it bare;
Yonder, huge bars of silver lay,
Dimm'd by the diamond's neighbouring ray,
Like the pale moon in morning day;
And in the midst four maidens stand,
The daughters of some distant land.
Their hue was of the dark-red dye,

That fringes oft a thunder sky;
Their hands palmetto baskets bare,
And cotton fillets bound their hair;
Slim was their form, their mien was shy,
To earth they bent the humbled eye,
Folded their arms, and suppliant kneel'd,
And thus their proffer'd gifts reveal'd.

CHORUS.

"See the treasures Merlin piled,
Portion meet for Arthur's child.
Bathe in Wealth's unbounded stream,
Wealth that avarice ne'er could dream!"

FIRST MAIDEN.

"See these clots of virgin gold!
Sever'd from the sparry mould,
Nature's mystic alchemy
In the mine thus bade them lie;
And their orient smile can win
Kings to stoop, and saints to sin."—

SECOND MAIDEN.

"See these pearls that long have slept;
These were tears by Naiads wept
For the loss of Marinel.
Tritons in the silver shell
Treasured them, till hard and white
As the teeth of Amphitrite."—

THIRD MAIDEN.

"Does a livelier hue delight?
Here are rubies blazing bright,
Here the emerald's fairy green,
And the topaz glows between;
Here their varied hues unite,
In the changeful chrysolite."—

FOURTH MAIDEN.

"Leave these gems of poorer shine,
Leave them all, and look on mine!
While their glories I expand,
Shade thine eyebrows with thy hand.
Mid-day sun and diamond's blaze

Blind the rash beholder's gaze."—

CHORUS.

"Warrior, seize the splendid store;
Would 'twere all our mountains bore!
We should ne'er in future story,
Read, Peru, thy perish'd glory!"

Calmly and unconcerned, the Knight
Waved aside the treasures bright:
"Gentle Maidens, rise, I pray!
Bar not thus my destined way.
Let these boasted brilliant toys
Braid the hair of girls and boys!
Bid your streams of gold expand
O'er proud London's thirsty land.
De Vaux of wealth saw never need,
Save to purvey him arms and steed,
And all the ore he deign'd to hoard
Inlays his helm and hilts his sword."
Thus gently parting from their hold,
He left, unmoved, the dome of gold.

And now the morning sun was high,
De Vaux was weary, faint, and dry;
When lo! a plashing sound he hears,
A gladsome signal that he nears
Some frolic water-run;
And soon he reach'd a court-yard square,
Where, dancing in the sultry air,
Toss'd high aloft, a fountain fair
Was sparkling in the sun.
On right and left, a fair arcade,
In long perspective view displayed
Alleys and bowers, for sun or shade:
But, full in front, a door,
Low-brow'd and dark, seem'd as it led
To the lone dwelling of the dead,
Whose memory was no more.

Here stopp'd De Vaux an instant's space,
To bathe his parched lips and face,
And mark'd with well-pleased eye,
Refracted on the fountain stream,

In rainbow hues, the dazzling beam
Of that gay summer sky.
His senses felt a mild control,
Like that which lulls the weary soul,
From contemplation high
Relaxing, when the ear receives
The music that the greenwood leaves
Make to the breezes' sigh.

And oft in such a dreamy mood,
The half-shut eye can frame
Fair apparitions in the wood,
As if the nymphs of field and flood
In gay procession came.
Are these of such fantastic mould,
Seen distant down the fair arcade,
These maids enlink'd in sister-fold,
Who, late at bashful distance staid,
Now tripping from the greenwood shade,
Nearer the musing champion draw,
And, in a pause of seeming awe,
Again stand doubtful now?—
Ah, that sly pause of witching powers!
That seems to say, "To please be ours,
Be yours to tell us how."
Their hue was of the golden glow
That suns of Candahar bestow,
O'er which in slight suffusion, flows
A frequent tinge of paly rose;
Their limbs were fashion'd fair and free,
In nature's justest symmetry;
And, wreathed with flowers, with odours graced,
Their raven ringlets reached the waist:
In eastern pomp, its gilding pale
The hennah lent each shapely nail,
And the dark sumah gave the eye
More liquid and more lustrous dye.
The spotless veil of misty lawn,
In studied disarrangement, drawn
The form and bosom o'er,
To win the eye, or tempt the touch,
For modesty show'd all too much—

Too much, yet promised more.

"Gentle Knight, a while delay,"
Thus they sung, "thy toilsome way,
While we pay the duty due
To our Master and to you.
Over Avarice, over Fear,
Love triumphant led thee here;
Warrior, list to us, for we
Are slaves to Love, are friends to thee.
Though no treasured gems have we,
To proffer on the bended knee,
Though we boast nor arm nor heart
For the assagay or dart,
Swains allow each simple girl
Ruby lip and teeth of pearl!
Or, if dangers more you prize,
Flatterers find them in our eyes.

"Stay, then, gentle Warrior, stay,
Rest till evening steal on day;
Stay, O, stay!—in yonder bowers
We will braid thy locks with flowers,
Spread the feast and fill the wine,
Charm thy ear with sounds divine,
Weave our dances till delight
Yield to languor, day to night.

"Then shall she you most approve,
Sing the lays that best you love,
Soft thy mossy couch shall spread,
Watch thy pillow, prop thy head,
Till the weary night be o'er—
Gentle Warrior, wouldst thou more?
Wouldst thou more, fair Warrior,—she
Is slave to Love and slave to thee."

O, do not hold it for a crime
In the bold hero of my rhyme.
For Stoic look,
And meet rebuke,
He lack'd the heart or time;
And round the band of sirens trip,
He kiss'd one damsel's laughing lip,

And press'd another's proffer'd hand,
Spoke to them all in accents bland,
But broke their magic circle through;
"Kind Maids," he said, "adieu, adieu!
My fate, my fortune, forward lies."
He said, and vanish'd from their eyes;
But, as he dared that darksome way,
Still heard behind their lovely lay:
"Fair Flower of Courtesy, depart!
Go, where the feelings of the heart
With the warm pulse in concord move;
Go, where Virtue sanctions Love!"

Downward De Vaux through darksome ways
And ruin'd vaults has gone,
Till issue from their wilder'd maze,
Or safe retreat, seem'd none,
And e'en the dismal path he strays
Grew worse as he went on.

For cheerful sun, for living air,
Foul vapours rise and mine-fires glare,
Whose fearful light the dangers show'd
That dogg'd him on that dreadful road.
Deep pits, and lakes of waters dun,
They show'd, but show'd not how to shun,
These scenes of desolate despair,
These smothering clouds of poison'd air,
How gladly had De Vaux exchanged,
Though 'twere to face yon tigers ranged!
Nay, soothful bards have said,
So perilous his state seem'd now,
He wish'd him under arbour bough
With Asia's willing maid.
When, joyful sound! at distance near
A trumpet flourish'd loud and clear,
And as it ceased, a lofty lay
Seem'd thus to chide his lagging way:—

"Son of Honour, theme of story,
Think on the reward before ye!
Danger, darkness, toil despise;
'Tis ambition bids thee rise.

"He that would her heights ascend,
Many a weary step must wend;
Hand and foot and knee he tries,
Thus ambition's minions rise.

"Lag not now, though rough the way,
Fortune's mood brooks no delay;
Grasp the boon that's spread before ye,
Monarch's power, and Conqueror's glory!"

It ceased. Advancing on the sound,
A steep ascent the Wanderer found,
And then a turret stair:
Nor climb'd he far its steepy round
Till fresher blew the air,
And next a welcome glimpse was given,
That cheer'd him with the light of heaven.
At length his toil had won
A lofty hall with trophies dress'd,
Where, as to greet imperial guest,
Four maidens stood, whose crimson vest
Was bound with golden zone.

Of Europe seem'd the damsels all;
The first a nymph of lively Gaul,
Whose easy step and laughing eye
Her borrow'd air of awe belie;
The next a maid of Spain,
Dark-eyed, dark-hair'd, sedate, yet bold;
White ivory skin and tress of gold,
Her shy and bashful comrade told
For daughter of Almaine,
These maidens bore a royal robe,
With crown, with sceptre, and with globe,
Emblems of empery;
The fourth a space behind them stood,
And leant upon a harp, in mood
Of minstrel ecstacy.
Of merry England she, in dress
Like ancient British Druidess:
Her hair an azure fillet bound,
Her graceful vesture swept the ground,
And, in her hand displayed,

A crown did that fourth Maiden hold,
But unadorned with gems and gold,
    Of glossy laurel made.

At once to brave De Vaux knelt down
    These foremost maidens three,
And proffer'd sceptre, robe, and crown,
    Liegedom and seignorie,
O'er many a region wide and fair,
Destined, they said, for Arthur's heir;
    But homage would he none:—
"Rather," he said, "De Vaux would ride,
A Warden of the Border-side,
In plate and mail, than, robed in pride,
    A monarch's empire own;
Rather, far rather, would he be,
A free-born knight of England free,
    Than sit on Despot's throne."
So pass'd he on, when that fourth Maid,
    As starting from a trance,
Upon the harp her finger laid;
Her magic touch the chords obey'd,
    Their soul awaked at once!

SONG OF THE FOURTH MAIDEN.

"Quake to your foundations deep,
Stately towers and banner'd keep,
Bid your vaulted echoes moan,
As the dreaded step they own.

"Fiends, that wait on Merlin's spell,
Hear the footfall! mark it well!
Spread your dusky wings abroad,
Bound ye for your homeward road!

"It is HIS, the first who e'er
Dared the dismal Hall of Fear;
His, who hath the snares defied
Spread by Pleasure, Wealth, and Pride.

"Quake to your foundations deep,
Bastion huge, and turret steep!
Tremble, keep! and totter, tower!
This is Gyneth's waking hour."

Thus while she sung, the venturous Knight
Has reach'd a bower, where milder light
    Through crimson curtains fell;
Such softened shade the hill receives,
Her purple veil when twilight leaves
    Upon its western swell.
That bower, the gazer to bewitch,
Had wondrous store of rare and rich
    As e'er was seen with eye;
For there, by magic skill, I wis,
Form of each thing that living is
    Was limn'd in proper dye.
All seemed to sleep—the timid hare
On form, the stag upon his lair,
The eagle in her eyrie fair
    Between the earth and sky.
But what of pictured rich and rare
Could win De Vaux's eye-glance, where,
Deep slumbering in the fatal chair,
    He saw King Arthur's child!
Doubt, and anger, and dismay
From her brow had passed away,
Forgot was that fell tourney-day,
    For, as she slept, she smiled:

It seem'd that the repentant Seer
Her sleep of many a hundred year
With gentle dreams beguiled.

That form of maiden loveliness,
'Twixt childhood and 'twixt youth,
That ivory chair, that sylvan dress,
The arms and ankles bare, express
Of Lyulph's tale the truth.
Still upon her garment's hem
Vanoc's blood made purple gem,
And the warder of command
Cumber'd still her sleeping hand;
Still her dark locks dishevelled low
From net of pearl o'er breast ofsnow;
And so fair the slumberer seems,
That De Vaux impeached his dreams,
Vapid all and void of might,
Hiding half her charms from sight.
Motionless a while he stands,
Folds his arm and clasps his hands,
Trembling in his fitful joy,
Doubtful how he should destroy
The long-enduring spell;
Doubtful, too, when slowly rise
Dark-fringed lids of Gyneth's eyes,
What these eyes shall tell,—
"St. George! St. Mary! can it be,
That they will kindly look on me!"

Gently, lo! the Warrior kneels,
Soft that lovely hand he steals,
Soft to kiss, and soft to clasp—
But the warder leaves her grasp;
Lightning flashes, rolls the thunder!
Gyneth startles from her sleep,
Totters tower, and trembles keep,
Burst the castle-walls asunder!
Fierce and frequent were the shocks,—
Melt the magic halls away;
——But beneath their mystic rocks,
In the arms of bold De Vaux
Safe the princess lay;

Safe and free from magic power,
Blushing like the rose's flower
    Opening to the day;
And round the Champion's brows were bound
The crown that Druidess had wound,
    Of the green laurel-bay.
And this was what remain'd of all
The wealth of each enchanted hall,
    Garland and the Dame:
But where should Warrior seek the meed,
Due to high worth for daring deed,
    Except from LOVE and FAME.

Our lovers, briefly be it said,
Wedded as lovers wont to wed,
    When tale or play is o'er;
Lived long and blest, loved fond andtrue,
And saw a numerous race renew
    The honours that they bore.
Know, too, that when a pilgrim strays,
In morning mist or evening maze,
    Along the mountain lone,
That fairy fortress often mocks
His gaze upon the castled rocks
    Of the Valley of St. John:
But never man since brave De Vaux
    The charmed portal won.
'Tis now a vain illusive show,
That melts whene'er the sunbeams glow,
    Or the fresh breeze hath blown.

THE END.